THE STORY OF

J ROBERT

OPPENHEIMER

THE STORY OF
J ROBERT
OPPENHEIMER

By Denise Royal

ST. MARTIN'S PRESS, NEW YORK

St. Martin's Press Inc.
175 Fifth Avenue New York N Y 10010

The Macmillan Company of Canada Limited
70 Bond Street Toronto 2

TO MY HUSBAND—

Through whose eyes I began to see
the beauty and excitement of science.

AND

TO NORMA YOUNGBERG—

A woman of unusual gifts and wisdom
who I am privileged to call "friend."

ACKNOWLEDGMENTS

First, I would like to express my deep gratitude to Dr. Harold H. Fisher, Professor Emeritus of Stanford University and retired Director of the Hoover Institution, for his understanding and for his valuable comments and suggestions on the historical material presented in this book. I am equally indebted to Dr. Edwin M. McMillan, Director of the Lawrence Radiation Laboratory at Berkeley for his editing of the scientific material and overall comments.

My gratefulness extends to those very busy men of science who took much of their time to give me invaluable help: Drs. Hans Bethe, Felix Bloch, Max Born, Robert Christy, E. U. Condon, Freeman Dyson, Frederick Koenig, Wolfgang Panofsky, I. I. Rabi, Leonard Schiff, Henry D. Smyth. Also I wish to thank Abraham Pais, Glenn Seaborg, Robert Serber, and Victor Weisskopf who made their Oppenheimer Memorial Addresses available to me. Through these men, I gained a better understanding of J Robert Oppenheimer and the wonder and enthusiasm he felt for physics.

For enlightenment, encouragement and information, I'm indebted to Professor Emeritus Raymond Birge, Mrs. Robert Brode, Professor Harold Cherniss of the Institute for Advanced Study, Professor Emeritus Will Dennes, Mr. Ralph Dimmick of the OAS, Dr. R. Hobart Ellis, editor of *Physics Today*, Professor Francis Fergusson, Mrs. Constance Goodman, Dr. Richard Hewlett, Chief Historian for the AEC, Professor George F. Kennan of the Institute for Advanced Study, Mr. William T. Kirk of SLAC, Mrs. Celeste Muschel of The Ethical Culture Schools, Mrs. Dorothy McKibbin, Miss Alberta Newton, Mr. Robert W. Newlin of the AEC, Mrs. Wolfgang Panofsky, Mr. Bill Richmond of the Los Alamos Scientific Laboratory, Mrs. Doris Stein of The Ethical Culture Schools, Mr. Franklin Tobey of the AEC, and the archivists and librarians of several public and university libraries.

I can only hint at the number and nature of my personal obligations to a number of men and women who, for reasons of their own, wish to remain nameless. To these individuals I owe my greatest debt. They not only started me in the right direction, but throughout the writing of this book, they made significant contributions. I want them to know how sincerely I appreciate their help, although I have no reason to believe that they, or others mentioned above, approve of this book in its entirety. I am solely responsible for the opinions and conclusions presented.

To my sons, Timothy and Jonathan, who showed patience and enthusiasm for this time-consuming project, I'm deeply grateful.

And finally, I cannot thank my husband, Frank Pearson, and Mrs. Norma Youngberg enough for their keen and illuminating criticism, endless encouragement, and understanding.

D. R.
Los Altos Hills, California

CONTENTS

AUTHOR'S NOTE

A tall, slightly stooped man walked through the doors of the White House Cabinet Room on a darkening winter afternoon. He wore the same frail, inquiring look that millions of people throughout the world had seen so often after the first atomic bomb fell on Hiroshima in 1945.

The man was Dr. J Robert Oppenheimer; the date, the second of December, 1963; the occasion, the seventh presentation of the Atomic Energy Commission's highest honor, the Enrico Fermi award: a gold medal, a citation, and a tax-free check for $50,000.

Lyndon B. Johnson, in one of his first official acts as President of the United States, made the presentation before a gathering of more than forty scientific and government leaders. Oppenheimer, overcome with emotion, grasped his wife's hand as he listened to the President commend him for his outstanding wartime leadership at Los Alamos.

When the President finished, Oppenheimer studied the citation. After several moments of silence, he looked up, then in a voice barely audible said, "I think it just possible, Mr. President, that it has taken some charity and some courage for you to make this award today. That would seem to me a good augury for all our futures."

Fraught with meaning, Oppenheimer's words can be understood only through a study of the man and his life—a highly complex man, and a life which symbolized many of the tragic dilemmas of the times. His life spanned the years of man's greatest achievement—the time of transition from man's dependence on energy from the sun, to man's ability to extract energy from the atom.

The influence of the times on the man, and the impact of the man on his times, form the story of J Robert Oppenheimer.

I

EARLY YEARS
(1900-1929)

1 ☙ THE CANVAS

ON A BITING JANUARY MORNING IN THE YEAR 1900, JULIUS
Oppenheimer, aged thirty, handsome, unmarried and rather
lonely, stared up at the sign over the door. Tall and slender, he
stood erect as a sentry at his post. For almost thirteen years he
had looked up at this sign as he walked through the door into the
building where he worked:

ROTHFELD, STERN & CO.
TEXTILE IMPORTERS
MANHATTAN, NEW YORK

Sol Rothfeld was his uncle. Julius had gone to work for
him when he first entered the United States as a German immi-
grant in 1887. Julius, only seventeen then, was overjoyed to
again see his older brother, Emil, who had preceded him to this
nation of energy and promise.

Many years earlier Julius had accomplished the first phase
of his cherished ambition—to become an American citizen. Now

on this January morning of the new century, he eagerly looked
forward to his first year as a full partner in the firm. He rejoiced
at his good fortune. There was much for which he was thankful:
He had entered into citizenship in America and also into its
world of business and economics.

Even before Julius had become a naturalized citizen he
recognized that his adopted land was not a static society. From
top to bottom each entity was under pressure both to improve
and expand. With the turn of the century the pioneering trait remained strong. Americans still had that independent spirit which
made them more tolerant, and more willing to ignore the old and
try the new. But of all American characteristics, the most promi-
nent was freedom of opportunity for the individual. American
thinking, social structure, and education made it easy for individuals to rise from the lowest ranks to positions of leadership
and enabled those in the highest ranks to retain their standing.

These were propitious times. With prosperity and peace favoring the western world, Americans turned a searchlight on
themselves and their civilization, and began to interpret the
world. Men turned more and more to culture; they searched for
a better understanding of the life around them. Julius Oppenheimer was one of these searching men.

Sol Rothfeld, quick to recognize his enterprising young
nephew's talents, taught Julius all he knew about textile importing. Julius, in turn, ventured beyond that which he had learned
and put to use many of his own ideas. They brought favorable
results. The business grew and prospered, and Julius had now become a partner in the firm.

This first month of the new century offered its varied op-
portunities to no more deserving man than Julius Oppenheimer.
Wall Street already knew him as a competent man of affairs and
an astute investor. He was known for his ability to see below the
surface, to look far into the future. But most of all, he was respected for his ability to keep his own counsel.

Julius Oppenheimer was no ordinary man. He had a look of sureness about him. Although his manner was sometimes bluff, it did not hide his warm-hearted, good-natured spirit. His humor was spontaneous, and always mirth-provoking.

There was something else about Julius Oppenheimer. He possessed an inexorable devotion to matters of the mind. He liked to read, not only books on history or politics, but also the classical works, and anything pertaining to the humanities. He frequented the New York museums, the theater, and loved to hear an opera or a concert. But most of all, he liked vigorous intellectual discussions on philosophy or ethics. He respected the dignity and worth of every human being; he treasured religious freedom and practiced religious tolerance. He cherished freedom of the mind, and thrived on intellectual challenge. These were legacies he would bequeath his sons.

Because Julius believed in man's worth, his dignity, and his possibilities, he naturally grew interested in the Ethical Culture Movement. Emil Oppenheimer and Sol Rothfeld were actively involved with the Movement and were members of the Society for Ethical Culture. In 1897, Julius joined the Society and became an active and dedicated member, serving on the Board of Trustees, off and on, for a period of twenty-nine years.

The Society for Ethical Culture was founded by Felix Adler on May 15, 1876. Adler, the son of a German rabbi, had advanced ideas of a society based on ethics rather than religious piety. Members of the Ethical Movement, as it was called, were basically "humanists in their practical labors, social vision and reform, humane ideals, and stress upon human capacities and dignity." They placed "man's relationship to his fellow man and his community at the center of their moral and spiritual quest." They believed "that man must assume responsibility for the direction of his life and destiny." Their maxim: "Diversity in the creed; unity in the deed."

During the years Julius Oppenheimer was active in the Society for Ethical Culture, he took part in many philanthropic and social reform movements—the erection of tenement houses to rid the city of unsafe, unsanitary, and overcrowded housing in the slums; in prison reforms and the abolition of capital punishment; in the prevention of discrimination of all sorts, and in civil liberties.

Then something happened. Julius lost his vitality, his lively sense of fun. He appeared distracted and tense. Sol Rothfeld tried to talk business with his nephew but Julius prefered to talk about maple buds falling, and tree branches crowned with calm leaves, slowly unfolding like golden promises. Sol Rothfeld threw up his hands. But while Sol oscillated between exasperation and anxiety, the women of the family just smiled and passed each other knowing glances. In their minds there was no doubt: Julius Oppenheimer was in love.

The reason for his distraction was a tall, slender, exquisite young lady named Ella Friedman, who had captivated Julius with her intellect and charm. She not only shared Julius' cultural interests, but was herself a gifted painter.

Ella must have seen Julius as the choice of her intellect and her heart, for in 1903 they married. Julius was affectionate and thoughtful, and deeply in love with his wife. Ella, in turn, sought always to make her husband comfortable and happy, and returned his love.

Julius Oppenheimer counted himself a happy, fortunate man. Times were good, business prospered, and his lovely wife was expecting their first child. One by one his most cherished dreams were coming true, and the future looked even more promising.

On April 22, 1904, Ella Friedman Oppenheimer gave birth to her first son. The proud parents named the boy J Robert Oppenheimer.* Much of the parents would be seen in the son—a fine legacy. At that moment, when Ella and Julius Oppenheimer

* The "J" in J Robert Oppenheimer is only an initial.

looked at their infant son, they could not possibly have known that he would be one of the moving forces that would shape the world. Nor did they know, or could they have known, that whatever their son would be—and he would be almost everything—he would also be its opposite.

2 ◐ CHILD PRODIGY

ROBERT GREW UP IN A SENSIBLE AND RELAXED HOUSEHOLD where the atmosphere was one of intellectual interests and cultural pursuits. For the first eight years of his life Robert and his parents lived in an apartment on West Ninety-fourth Street in New York City. His mother, Ella, made their home a place of grace and comfort. She saw to it that fresh flowers, good music, and stimulating conversation enriched the family's everyday life. She also made certain that she spent an hour or more each day with her son. She would read to him, teach him about art, or take him to an art exhibit or a museum, or they would just sit together, talking about his ideas and interests.

The boy inherited more than his sensitivity and good looks from his mother. She gave him her ardency and emotional intensity, enthusiasm for all he undertook. Furthermore, Ella Oppenheimer was a good listener, an encouraging audience for Robert.

This may be why Robert is said to have been something of a conversationalist even before he reached school age. Ella encouraged her son to mull over his ideas, to spin them into the fine tapestry of his thinking. This he did well; his mind imbibed like a sponge. Robert learned to think for himself, and his thinking sparkled with originality. Once when he was four years old he went to Christmas mass at Saint Patrick's Cathedral with the family's Irish nurse. When he returned home he commented, "They are celebrating the birthday of that noble Irishman, Jesus Christ."

Always Robert stood apart from his peers. When boys his age wanted to be policemen or firemen, Robert became interested in ancient and modern buildings and announced that he was going to be an architect. His parents thought this a splendid idea and provided him with photographs and prints of the world's architectural masterpieces and with books on architecture that he could barely read. But before he reached the age of seven, Robert changed his mind. He decided to be a poet. His parents then rushed out and bought him works of the classical poets, and Robert scribbled verses on the unlimited pads of paper provided by his mother. Then one day, while watching his mother working at her canvas, Robert suddenly wanted to become a great artist. Soon, he was working at his own little easel with his own box of oils and sable brushes. Before long he could discuss art theories with his parents. Robert Oppenheimer did not become an artist, but throughout his life he appreciated art and had a great admiration for the work of the Impressionist painters, saying, "Their elegance of form intrigues me."

Robert's memory astonished everyone. No matter what he heard or read, he could relate it back, almost word for word. Before he was six, he delighted his music-loving parents by recognizing even the most obscure selections from the symphonies of the great composers. Also his vocabulary amazed all who knew him. He was not just mimicking grown-up words he heard, for if asked, Robert could explain the meaning of every word he used.

Like most young children, Robert liked to rhyme words. But he carried his rhyming a little further. When he first started studying Latin, he'd walk about chanting, "pingo, pingere, pinxi, pictus," the Latin verb "paint." He enjoyed the sounds of the words.

Julius delighted in passing on much of his knowledge of history by telling Robert about Europe. He also took his son abroad four times before Robert reached college age.

Robert's interest in science began during one of these trips to Europe. When he was five years old, he visited his grandfather in Germany and was given a box of minerals as a gift. From then on Robert searched for new specimens wherever he went. He became so interested in the crystal collection at the Natural History Museum that the curator took him as a pupil. Under his guidance Robert's crystal collection grew so extensive that additional space had to be found for the ever growing aggregation. In time, the Oppenheimer hallway looked like a quarry.

As his knowledge of minerals increased, Robert grew interested in the rock formations in Central Park. He began corresponding with several well-known geologists. He had already learned to use the family typewriter and typed his letters. This skill, together with his amazing facility with language, deceived many of the experts with whom he corresponded. They never realized they were communicating with an eleven-year-old boy.

One of these men put up Robert's name for membership in the New York Mineralogical Club. It came as quite a surprise when Robert received a letter from the organization telling him that he had been accepted for membership.

Robert maintained a steady correspondence with many of the club members and at the age of twelve, he was invited to deliver a lecture before the club. Young Robert pleaded with his

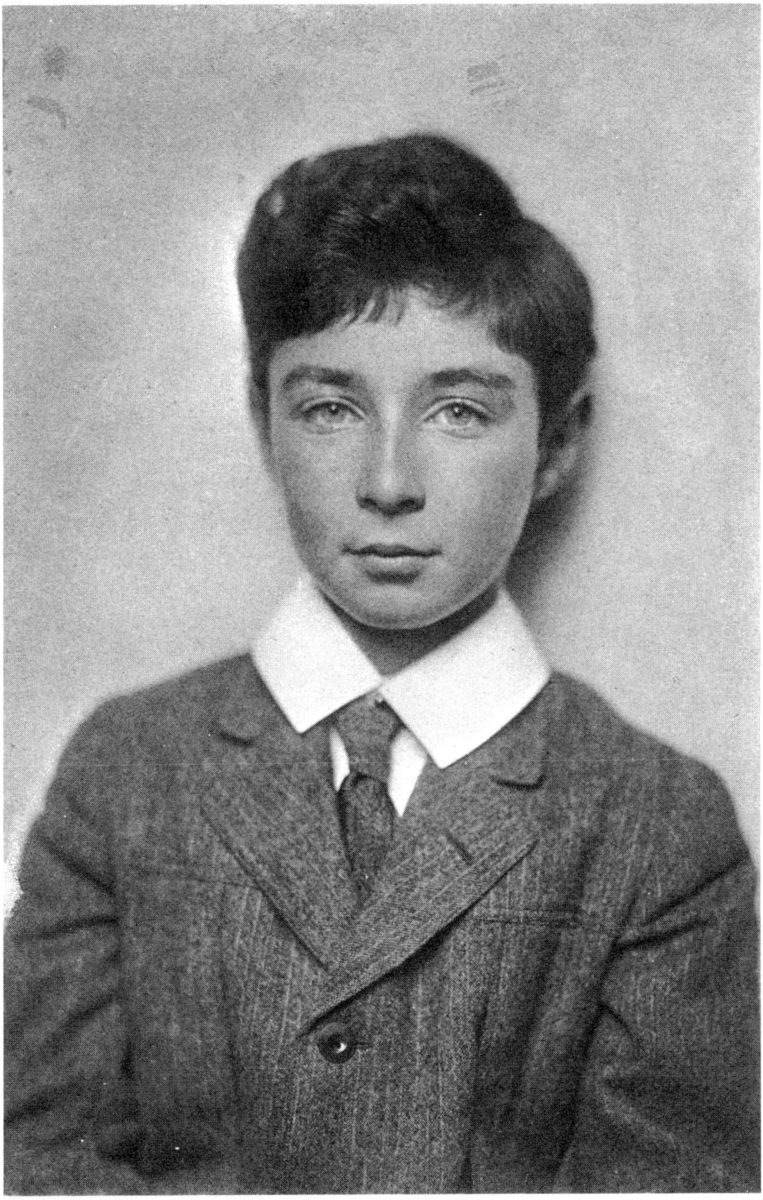

Robert Oppenheimer at age nine

father to tell them he was ill; tell them he was only twelve years old; tell them anything! Robert had stage fright! But Julius Oppenheimer's pride was mixed with wisdom. He'd not hear of it. He had complete confidence in his son's abilities.

The appointed evening arrived. Accompanied by his mother and father, Robert found himself at the club's quarters at a West Side New York hotel. An usher met the Oppenheimers and Julius proudly announced that his son was the principal speaker for the evening. After much discussion Julius convinced the man that his son was "J Robert Oppenheimer."

At last the chairman was convinced of the boy's identity, and the proceedings got under way. He introduced Robert to the members. But as the boy stepped behind the speaker's podium, a flurry of amusement broke out in the audience. Even Ella Oppenheimer laughed, for all that could be seen of Robert were two bright blue eyes and a head of dark curly hair. Someone hurriedly found a box for him to stand on, and Robert began his prepared speech. A burst of applause broke out in the audience and Robert almost lost his little remaining composure. But when he looked at his beaming parents, he smiled and went bravely on.

Although the Oppenheimers were both amused by Robert's interest in minerals, and encouraged by his apparent bent toward the sciences, the keenly observant parents began to wonder if there was something more meaningful in Robert's behavior. The intensity of his interests, and his ability to take his collection seriously, were unusual in a child his age. Could their son be even brighter than they had suspected? Might he be a genius? The parents didn't know. They were certain of only one thing: Robert should be given every opportunity to explore and develop his potentialities. They had already taken the first step in this direction. With their interest in the Ethical Culture Movement and their active participation in the Society for Ethical Culture, they enrolled Robert in The Ethical Culture School in midtown Manhattan.

Also founded by Felix Adler, The Ethical Culture School grew out of the first free kindergarten in New York City. "Ethical," as it is often called, offered a new kind of education, with courses in craft and art work, geography, history, nature study, shop work, the writing of original compositions, singing, games, sports, excursions, and dramatics, along with "the three R's." Such a rich and varied curriculum was a startling innovation in those days. The ideas and practices contrasted sharply with the huge classes, strict routines and rote learning of schools throughout the United States. Today, "Ethical's" scholastic standing is ranked by educators as one of the finest in the world.

The school, in its early years, developed a new progressive attitude toward science teaching. The first head of the school, Henry A. Kelly, who had been curator of the Museum of Natural History in Massachusetts, believed that every child should be considered a "potential scientist." On this premise he operated the science program.

Robert Oppenheimer benefited from Kelly's belief. He already had a natural, eager, unbounded curiosity about his world. Before he was eight, his science course at "Ethical" allowed him to expand his interest in minerals by offering him both indoor and outdoor laboratory work. Outdoors, he collected rocks and observed geological formations; indoors, he classified, discussed, experimented, and reported on his findings.

In the third grade Robert had regular laboratory time where he received guidance on special projects. From the fourth grade on, he kept science notebooks where he recorded his observations and conclusions. And by the time he reached fifth grade, he had begun individual work in elementary physics.

Besides the wealth of unique subjects offered by the school, it was to have a profound effect on Robert's life. His thinking, his approach to people and problems, and his complete revulsion toward discrimination of any kind can all be traced back to the philosophy of The Ethical Culture School.

Along with his interest in the sciences, Robert also enjoyed literature. He picked up languages, French in particular, with considerable ease and he continued painting and writing poetry. Because Robert's parents were so eager to give him all the cultural things in life, and he was intelligent enough to absorb this knowledge, Robert missed the fun most children have. Those who knew him well say he seldom spoke of his childhood with fond recollection. He often said, "I was an unctuous, repulsively good little boy."

Although not mentioned in other accounts of his life, Robert's frail health may have prevented him from playing much with other children. Robert was subject to frequent colds, and after the loss of his brother Lewis, who died shortly after birth, his parents fretted anxiously about him. A childhood friend said, "When J Robert was young he was frequently ill and as a consequence his parents would permit him to play with few children for fear of exposure to additional childhood diseases. Therefore, he developed other interests, including experimenting with his microscope and gathering minerals. . . ."

Robert did not play with the usual boys' toys. His favorite plaything was a laboratory miscroscope given him by his father. Young Robert spent hours viewing everything that would fit on the microscope stage.

As the boy grew older, his parents became more convinced that Robert was a genius. Had he not displayed all the signs; his easy recognition of obscure selections of classical music; the ease with which he learned foreign languages; his far-reaching interest in all areas of science? And besides, he had no regard for the things that interested most children. He was never noisy, never got into mischief.

Robert had learned good manners. Although he might be provoked into thinking something rude, harsh, or improper, he was never permitted to express it. He never violated the family standard of courtesy. Even in his later years, many people recall his saying, "One can never be too courteous." But also in his later years, Robert recalled, "My childhood did not prepare me for the fact that the world is full of cruel and bitter things." As he saw it, his home had offered him "no normal, healthy way to be a bastard."

He grew up with a great deal of love from parents devoted to the pursuit of culture. They recognized their son's potentialities, and were affluent enough to provide him with all that was needed to nourish his bright mind. Even so, Robert once recalled in horror, "I repaid my parents' confidence in me by developing an unpleasant ego which I am sure must have affronted both children and adults who were unfortunate enough to come into contact with me."

But if Robert had an offensive self-conceit, his teachers and parents tolerated it because of his genius. The very brilliance of his mind gave Robert the center of the stage, a spot to which he would grow accustomed.

In the year 1912 two changes occurred in Robert's life. First, the Oppenheimers moved to a sunny nine-room apartment at 155 Riverside Drive. Then on August 14, 1912, the second change came into Robert's life. The arrival of a baby brother, Frank Friedman Oppenheimer, filled the household with excitement. For a time Robert forgot his other interests and joined the family in caring for the new baby. Robert took great pride in Frank's every accomplishment. He continued to view his younger brother with the same pride as Frank grew up, while Frank looked up to his brother, who protected and encouraged him. Of his relationship with his brother, Robert said, "I think I was both an older brother and in some ways perhaps part of a father to him because of that age difference. We were close during our childhood, although the age gap made our interests different. . . ." But Frank, like Robert, would decide to study physics. Julius and Ella Oppenheimer considered them-

 *Robert and Frank Oppenheimer*

selves indeed fortunate; they had not only one son, but two, who showed promise of brilliant futures.

Julius Oppenheimer's business, the importing of materials used in linings of men's suits and jackets, flourished. More and more, he was able to provide his family with the best of everything. In the way of toys, hobbies, or amusements for children, nothing existed that the boys could not have.

Only once did the Oppenheimers' efforts to give Robert all the cultural advantages backfire. Robert took piano lessons for a number of years. Once when he was ill with the flu, his mother asked him how he felt. "Like I do when I have to practice the piano," Robert answered. That ended the piano lessons.

3 ☯ THE LONER

ROBERT TURNED FOURTEEN IN APRIL OF 1918, AND, AS WOULD be true a good part of his life, his intellectual maturity far exceeded his emotional maturity. Although he had friends, he felt alone most of the time. Even among his bright peers at The Ethical Culture School Robert did not fit well. First of all, he was not athletic. Although not all of his classmates were adept at sports, they did take part in the activities. But Robert had no aptitude for sports. No matter how hard he tried, he did worse than the worst.

Too, Robert was shy. In conversation he fared only slightly better than he did in sports. He'd join in when the talk was intellectual. He appeared happy to do so. "But when the discourse changed to lighter matters," a classmate recalls, "Robert retreated emotionally." His peers mistook his shyness for boredom —boredom with them and their discussion. They called him a "snob." In contrast, when the conversation was intellectually lively, and Robert chimed in, he was thought to be a "showoff." He reasoned more rapidly, and, in general, knew more about the subject than his classmates. He became so engrossed in the topic that he dominated the conversation. But it was not pomposity that prompted Robert to act in such a manner. He would have been aghast if he had realized how his peers interpreted his actions.

Perhaps his parent felt a boys' camp would help Robert find his way with other children, for they arranged to have him spend that summer at Camp Koenig, near Clayton, New York.

The camp was founded by, named after, and operated under the directorship of Dr. Otto Koenig. A distinguished educator in American secondary education, Koenig, a Gentile, was also the principal of a Jewish boys' school, the Sachs Collegiate Institute in New York City.

No one seems to know how Robert felt about going to camp. But the Oppenheimers were not the kind of parents who would have forced summer camp on their son had he not wished to go.

During his early weeks at camp, Robert met the Director's son, Frederick. "We became rather friendly because of our mutual interest in minerals. I, too, had quite an extensive collection," Fred Koenig recalled. Koenig, now Doctor Koenig, Professor of Chemistry at Stanford University in California, thought back to that summer prior to the end of World War I: "Robert and I took hikes, searching for new rock specimens. We talked as we walked. I remember Robert quoting passage after passage of George Eliot. He found her conviction that there is a cause and effect relationship in human behavior, as well as in nature —her awareness of fate—to be quite fascinating. We discussed this at length."

Professor Koenig remembered Robert Oppenheimer as "bright and sensitive, but very much in conflict with himself— the conflict between thought and action. For some reason,"

Koenig said, "when I think of Oppenheimer a quote from Goethe comes to mind:

> Thought widens, but paralyzes; whereas
> action enlivens, but narrows."

Several people have voiced the opinion that Robert Oppenheimer had a "Messiah complex." Fred Koenig shares this opinion, but his view is supported by facts known to few.

"Of course, I could be wrong," Koenig says, "but I often felt that what happened to Robert in camp that summer could easily account for much of his behavior—his actions—that people found so baffling. I don't see how an experience such as he had could have been anything but traumatic."

At camp, as at school, Robert was a square peg in a round hole. He wrote his parents daily, which brought jibes from the other boys. And when they learned that he wrote poetry, their mockery knew no end. They ran through a long list of derogatory names, which, in most instances, would have resulted in black eyes, bloody noses, and cut lips. But Robert was no fighter. Both his background and training had encouraged use of the mind, not the fists. The boys, at last, decided upon "Cutie" as their choice name for Robert. They called him little else. But if the boys' taunting reached Robert, and it no doubt did, he deigned no reply. His attitude only incited his tormentors.

The singling out of those who are different has long been a sadistic sport of man. What was different about Robert Oppenheimer? He was of Jewish extraction, but, except for Fred Koenig, so were the rest of the boys. Robert came from a wealthy family; the other boys also came from wealthy families. Obviously, the difference lay in Robert himself.

"Robert enjoyed being different," recalls Fred Koenig. "He was an intellectual snob, a mental exhibitionist. Because of this, to some extent, he asked for it."

For a time things were bad, but they grew worse. Mere name-calling no longer satisfied the tormentors. They tired of verbal taunts. But as it happened, so hideous was their malice that no amount of intellectual snobbery or exhibitionism could ever justify their actions.

Knowing that Robert took evening walks, they lay in wait for him and when he passed they captured him and dragged him off to the icehouse where "they stripped him of his clothes and tortured him." Fred Koenig recalled an account of the incident he had heard. "They, as it were, crucified him."

As a final touch to their torture, "they painted his derriere green, along with other parts of his anatomy."

In spite of the fiendish attack, Robert remained at camp. "I don't know how Robert stuck out those remaining weeks," says Koenig. "Not many boys would have—or could have—but Robert did. It must have been hell for him."

He never, through the remainder of his life, mentioned his experience at Camp Koenig.

Robert returned to The Ethical Cultural School that fall more depressed than ever. If genius has a price, Robert Oppenheimer paid his price in loneliness. To his favorite English teacher, Herbert Winslow Smith, Robert confided, "I'm the loneliest man in the world."

The last Ethical Culture teacher who is known to have had considerable influence on Robert was Augustus Klock. Klock is best described by Robert himself when, upon Klock's death in 1963, he wrote:

"It is almost forty-five years since Augustus Klock taught me physics and chemistry, but I have not forgotten, and do not expect to forget, the two winters, and above all the summer I spent with him. He loved these sciences . . . and the view of nature—part order, part puzzle, that is the condition of science. But above all he loved young people, to whom he hoped to give some touch, some taste, some love of life, and in whose awakening he saw his destiny."

The two winters Robert speaks of were his junior and senior years at Ethical. It was during this time that Robert was first introduced to the atomic theory, which he is reported to have found "a very exciting experience."

The summer spent with Augustus Klock was to be a memorable one for Robert in many ways. By this time Julius Oppenheimer was convinced that Robert was a genius, and "had begun to consider his son as a kind of public trust." He had arranged for Klock to give Robert an advanced course in chemistry. In six weeks Robert completed the one-year course.

So pleased was Julius Oppenheimer with his son's progress that he bought the boy a twenty-seven-foot sloop, which Robert christened *Trimethy,* after the chemical trimethylene chloride.

Now that Robert had the *Trimethy* he no longer cared to sail with his parents on their boat. Unfortunately, Robert lacked sailing experience, and his first summer as "Captain" caused him some embarrassment. Once he and Frank decided to dock at Cherry Grove on Fire Island. They had ample mooring area, but Robert failed to point the bow of the boat into the wind at the right moment. While he retreated to maneuver a second try, a little girl wandered onto the dock and stood watching the operation with great interest. Robert started to glide in. Frank readied the mooring line. When docking, a sailboat heads into the wind and lets the sail act as a brake. This allows the boat to coast in and touch the dock lightly. But Robert misjudged the wind direction and gained too much momentum. He slammed into the dock with such force that he knocked the child into the water.

The girl climbed out of the water and after the boys were certain she was uninjured, "we were so embarrassed, that we turned around and sailed off," Frank recalls.

For Robert and Frank sailing was a peaceful and stimulating sport most of the time. They sailed the blue waters of the Great South Bay and relaxed in its tranquillity. But one day Robert decided to explore the inlets of Long Island Sound. Most seasoned sailors know that there are waters along the Sound that are best avoided. Robert didn't. Filled with a sense of high adventure he happily sailed the *Trimethy* into an unfamiliar inlet. The thought of running aground never entered his mind. But that was what he did—run aground. Stranded on a mud bank! Hours passed. The boys waited. There was not another boat in sight. The brothers got hungry, while the gnats had a fine feed. Evening came, gray and cold with still no help in sight. Robert tried to cheer his brother.

Back at the house, the Oppenheimers worried. More time passed, and with its passing even Julius Oppenheimer weakened. Finally, he agreed to get help. He prevailed upon the Coast Guard officers, commonly called "Revenuers," to search for his missing sons.

Within a short time the Revenuers found Robert and Frank on their mud-flat prison and towed them in. The boys were so humiliated, however, that had they not been so cold and hungry they would have regretted their rescue. The next day Julius presented Robert with a set of local sailing charts and suggested that his son turn his studies to the charts for the time being.

Robert graduated as valedictorian in February of 1921. Although only seventeen, he had mastered five languages and had done college level work in math, chemistry, physics, Greek, and Latin. The Oppenheimers planned a holiday in Europe, but while waiting for Frank to complete his school year, Robert returned to Ethical to do more advanced work. Sometime between his birthday and the first of May, Robert suffered an appendicitis attack and had to undergo surgery.

The popular belief is that the Oppenheimers' trip to Europe was to contemplate Robert's future. But Robert, himself, had chosen Harvard and had already been accepted.

Robert recuperated rapidly and the Oppenheimers left for Europe that June. Frank Oppenheimer recalls, "Robert and I would roam around all day, seeing the sights, or hunting for mineral specimens."

Fall and Harvard approached. Then Robert contracted dysentery. The trip had to be cut short and he had to be sent home on a stretcher. All that fall of 1921, Robert fought to regain his strength. Although somewhat victorious in his battle, he was not well enough to enter Harvard that year. He'd have to delay his college education for a year, the doctors said. Then they advised the worried parents to remove Robert from the cold, damp winters of New York. What he needed was good clean air, plenty of sunshine and rest. They recommended that the young man be sent West.

Julius Oppenheimer engaged Ethical teacher Herbert Smith to act as Robert's companion and shortly after Christmas, Robert and Smith left for the Page Dude Ranch near Cowles, New Mexico.

From his first glance, New Mexico, held Robert's heart. The land was alive with warmth and color and it breathed its life into Robert. He spent long hours searching for mineral specimens; he learned to sit a horse with a Western saddle; he hiked; and he and Smith are said to have dressed like prospectors and talked like philosophers. Under the watchful eye of Mrs. Katherine Page, the ranch owner, Robert gained weight, his spirit returned, and his health improved. By the end of spring the old restlessness returned. His spirit and body had been nourished, now he longed to satify the cravings of his hungry mind. He returned home, spent the summer at Bayshore where he sailed the *Trimethy,* read, relaxed, and regaled his family with stories, both serious and humorous, of life in the West. Robert promised himself that he would return to New Mexico. But that would come later. Now Robert looked to his more immediate future: Harvard College.

4 ⊗ A STIR IN THE COCOON

IN SEPTEMBER 1922, EIGHTEEN-YEAR-OLD J ROBERT OPPEN-heimer entered Harvard College. Then, as now, Harvard encouraged its students to enroll in the most advanced courses for which they qualified. In every area, Robert qualified as a sophomore. The unusual amount of advanced work he had done at Ethical Culture High School as well as his entrance examinations presented convincing evidence of his superior mind.

Harvard offered Robert the kind of atmosphere he thrived on. He likened himself to a Goth coming into Rome. Why did he consider himself a Goth? "Just as the Goths descended on Rome, Robert plunged into the stacks at Widener Library," a Harvard classmate explains. "He intellectually looted the place."

Again, the records testify to the intensity with which Robert threw himself into his work. He spent hours in the chemistry laboratory, followed by even longer hours in the library. He

was just beginning to learn the art of self-discipline and six
years later, when his brother Frank was preparing for college,
he wrote:

Dear Frank,

. . . You put a hard question on the virtue of discipline.
What you say is true; I do value it and—I think that you do
too—more than for its earthly fruit, proficiency. I think that
one can give only a metaphysical ground for this evaluation;
but the variety of metaphysics which give an answer to your
question has been very great, the metaphysics themselves very
disparate: the Bhagavad Gita, Ecclesiastes, the Stoa, the beginning of the Laws, Hugo of St. Victor, John of the Cross,
Spinoza. This very great disparity suggests that the fact that
discipline is good for the soul is more fundamental than any
of the grounds given for its goodness. I believe that through
discipline, though not through discipline alone, we can achieve
serenity, and a certain small but precious measure of freedom
from the accidents of incarnation, and charity, and that detachment which preserves the world which it renounces. I believe that through discipline we learn to preserve what is essential to our happiness in more and more adverse circumstances,
and to abandon with simplicity what would else have seemed
to us indispensable; that we come a little to see the world without the gross distortion of personal desire, and in seeing it so,
accept more easily our earthly privation and its earthly horror.
. . . But because I believe that the reward of discipline is
greater than its immediate objective, I would not have you
think that discipline without objective is possible: in its nature
discipline involves the subjection of the soul to some perhaps
minor end; and that end must be real, if the discipline is not to
be factitious: study, and our duties to men and to the com-
monwealth, war, and personal hardship, and even the need for
subsistence, ought to be greeted by us with profound gratitude;
for only through them can we attain to the least detachment;
and only so can we know peace. . . .

At Harvard Robert developed the intense concentration
which would mark him through life. But all these rigid dis-
ciplines made him something of a snob. He had a few close
friends. With them he'd debate and discuss everything from philosophy to girls. Beyond this circle, however, he remained shy;

he didn't mix much, and when he did he was unable to give himself easily to intimacies.

Robert's health problem continued. The dysentery had left him with colitis which would take years to cure. After considerable thought, he decided upon a special diet to speed his recovery. One item on his diet was raisin-filled chocolate bars, which do not sound unpalatable, but with this confection, "he swallowed a considerable amount of mineral oil," a friend recalls.

During Robert's second year at Harvard, he warmed a little. His wit and sense of humor showed more frequently and for the first time in his life he became what he called "a social animal." But his studies were never forgotten. He carried seven courses and a number of electives and still found time to read Dante, to delve into French literature, to dip into Chinese, and he began to wade deeply in philosophy.

In his junior year, Robert realized that he had majored in the wrong subject. His real interest, he discovered, was in physics. At this juncture, he sought out physicist Percy Bridgman. He presented his problem to Bridgman, telling the gruff, honest professor that he was taking six courses, auditing four, and still did not have enough to keep him busy. Then he told Bridgman that his real interest, he thought, lay in physics, not chemistry, his major. Bridgman studied Robert. Was this young man veracious, or arrogant? Or was he both? No one knows what conclusion Bridgman reached, but he answered Robert by saying, "Sit in my class and we'll see what happens."

Robert proved to be both honest and egotistic. Bridgman soon realized he had admitted a budding physicist to his class, and one of considerable promise. He tutored Robert, encouraged him, and more than once became infuriated with him. Once at Bridgman's home, the professor showed Robert some photographs of ancient architecture.

"This is a picture of the temple at Segesta, Sicily, built around 400 B.C.," said Bridgman.

Robert's answer came calmly and confidently. "I'm sorry to contradict you about the date." He leaned forward and pointed to the columns. "But it had to be built at least fifty years earlier. This you can tell by the spiral volutes of the capital."

Later Bridgman was able to laugh about the incident.

Bridgman didn't laugh at Robert in the laboratory, however; he was aghast. "How can such a brilliant student be so clumsy?" he asked. Robert not only fumbled and broke things; he could not make the simplest experiment work, when by all natural laws it should have. When it came to theory, Robert excelled. He immediately grasped the concept, formulated equations, and had usually arrived at a conclusion by the time Bridgman finished presenting the problem. Bridgman recognized his pupil's ability for fast mental gymnastics, and nurtured it. He allowed Robert to go beyond the experiment itself and encouraged him to think and talk the problem out.

In that same year, 1924, another great man entered Robert's life. Philosopher Albert North Whitehead, already a man of sixty-three, arrived in Cambridge, Massachusetts, where he served as professor of philosophy until his retirement ten years later.

Whitehead's fame had preceded him to Harvard and Robert eagerly awaited the opportunity to meet the brilliant philosopher. After the two met, they spent long hours discussing how philosophy and poetry are akin. Robert understood what Whitehead meant when he said that in both philosophy and poetry "there is a reference to form beyond the direct meanings of words." Until now, the relationship between poetry and philosophy had been only something Robert intuitively felt. Now Whitehead explained that "poetry allies itself to nature, philosophy to mathematic patterns."

During Robert's last year at Harvard he took a total of ten courses. He originally registered for six, but finding additional time on his hands, he audited four more and took exams in all ten. He enjoyed the challenge to his mind, the pitting of his brain against the intelligence of others. He is quoted as saying he liked exams because of "the definiteness and excitement."

When he was notified that he headed his class and would graduate *summa cum laude,* Robert, although pleased and proud, looked upon himself as a valedictorian without an identity.

In later years Robert spoke of his Harvard experience as the "most exciting time I've ever had in my life. I really had a chance to learn. I loved it. I almost came alive." For the first time in his life, Robert had accumulated sufficient years. No longer a boy, he had reached a degree of maturity which enabled him to associate with men who, along with knowledge, possessed wisdom—the wisdom found only with age and experience in living. To be fully alive, in his way of thinking, he must compare with the best of the minds that surrounded him. He had not yet attained this stature.

5 ❧ NEW KNOWLEDGE
IN THE OLD WORLD

ROBERT TURNED TWENTY-ONE SEVERAL MONTHS BEFORE GRAD-
uation. Now that he had reached manhood, Julius Oppenheimer
presented his son with a considerable sum of money, telling him
he could do with it as he saw fit. Robert looked at his father;
words caught in his throat. At last he said, "I'd better not take
the money."

"Why not?"

"Because I may not turn out to be the kind of person you
approve of," Robert answered.

Julius studied his son. "If that's true, then it won't be the
money I'll worry about."

Robert accepted the gift.

The day of graduation arrived. When he put on his cap and
gown Robert laughed. "I'd make a fine scarecrow!" Those
present had to agree. His cap was too large and persisted in
slipping down around his ears, and his gown hung in deep folds

on his lean six-foot frame. But something else is remembered more than the cap and gown. A light shone in Robert's eyes, "as though he were looking beyond the day."

The next step in the education of J Robert Oppenheimer had been arranged many months before his graduation from Harvard.

While many American men of science had gone to sleep with classical physics, some had kept a watchful eye turned toward the Old World where startling new discoveries were occurring. Percy Bridgman was one of the latter. He did not agree with his colleagues who told their students, "We have reached the end in physics. All that remains is to refine our measuring techniques."

While this prognosis was true of classical physics, these men had ignored two great revolutionary theories presented in the first decades of the new century: the *Theory of Relativity* and the *Quantum Theory*.

The Relativity Theory was mainly the creation of one man, Albert Einstein, and had come in two installments: the Special Theory of Relativity, published in 1905, and the General Theory, published in 1915.

Einstein's Theory of Relativity called for radical changes in the classical concept of space and time as two independent entities. Time is regarded as a fourth coordinate, though it is not quite equivalent to the three space coordinates. Space and time become interconnected, so that their measurement is no longer independent. The Special Theory of Relativity introduced important changes in the treatment of the motion of electrons in an atom, while the General Theory deals with motion on a large scale, like that of galaxies in the universe.

The Quantum Theory, on the other hand, is the result of the creative work of several great scientists starting with Max Planck, who in 1899 walked to the blackboard at the Christmas meeting of the German Physical Society and proposed an extraordinary hypothesis. Planck said that energy radiation was not continuous. Instead, that energy was emitted in the form of little bundles, or packets, which he called "energy elements."

While Planck's notion of "energy elements" served only as the basis for statistical energy distribution among different wave lengths in the radiation from a hot body, it took a broader meaning in the hands of the young Albert Einstein. Six years later, in one of the three articles published by him in that year, Einstein applied the idea of light *quanta* to the explanation of the so-called "photo-electric effect." With Einstein's suggestion, Planck's hypothesis became accepted as a theory of wide significance.

Twenty years after Einstein's 1905 paper, de Broglie, Heisenberg, Schrödinger, Dirac, Pauli, Born, and many others initiated one of the greatest theoretical efforts in the history of science, in which the old Quantum Theory was developed into the modern Quantum Mechanics, which has altered all of physics. Oppenheimer was to become deeply involved in this effort and make important contributions.

In the summer of 1925, at the age of 21, Robert Oppenheimer sailed for the Old World and the New Physics. Before Robert left, Bridgman is reported to have told him, "You cannot be satisfied with just measuring up with other people. You can consider yourself a failure unless you stand out in front."

Armed with his honors from Harvard and a recommendation from Percy Bridgman, Robert arrived at the famed Cavendish Laboratory in Cambridge, England. Here, for one year, Robert met and worked with many of the scientific giants destined to remake the world: Lord Ernest Rutherford, the Director of the Laboratory and also the man who had developed the model of the nuclear atom in 1911; the tall, rather stiff P. M. S. Blackett, the man who would later photograph and interpret the miraculous world of atomic events; Paul Dirac, the "ivory tower" scientist, who was always willing to chat about any ordinary topic, but who preferred to pursue his studies alone; and with Niels Bohr, who needed only to announce that he intended to lecture at some university on his recent findings to make every physicist within a reasonable distance do everything in his power to attend. Bohr's warm personality and creative genius made him the most remarkable of men. Robert's admiration for Bohr bordered on veneration. One of Oppenheimer's philosophical tenets was Bohr's principle of complementarity.

At Cavendish there were no teachers and pupils, only men working closely together, helping one another assess the unknown and incomplete. It didn't seem to matter to anyone that Robert was again completely inept in the laboratory, for at theory he excelled.

At Cambridge Robert was accepted as an intellectual equal. Yet this acceptance was not enough. Robert, himself, knew that while he approached intellectual maturity, he remained emotionally immature. Filled with depression and doubt, he realized that he could no longer postpone the "problem of growing up." From his own words one sees evidence of deep inner struggles and anxieties: "My feeling about myself was always one of extreme discontent. I had very little sensitiveness to human beings, very little humility before the realities of this world." Characteristically, he turned to books for the answer to "Who am I?" He read Dostoevsky, Proust, and St. Thomas Aquinas.

Along with his reading, Robert explored the defects in his own character. By early December Robert had sunk into even greater depression. It is at this time that he considered ending it all. In his own words, "I was on the point of bumping myself off. This was chronic." But apparently Robert realized, as all men do who have traveled along the path to self-knowledge, that development comes in stages.

According to an informant, shortly before Christmas Robert received a note from Jefferies Wyman, a Harvard friend, asking Robert to join him in Corsica for the holidays. For more than a week, the pair renewed their friendship, reviewed old times, talked of the future, and explored the island. Coming out of this last period of self-examination he said, "I felt much kinder and more tolerant. I could now relate to others. . . ." Robert had come a long way, but he now knew and accepted, that to complete the journey would take a lifetime.

Near the end of the holiday, Wyman urged Robert to travel along with him to Rome, where Francis Fergusson and Fred Koenig, also Harvard graduates, were visiting. "I'd like to, but I can't," Robert told Wyman, his expression growing more serious. "I have to get to Cambridge."

"Why?" asked Wyman. "There's plenty of time left."

A twinkle shown in Robert's eyes. "I left a poison apple on Blackett's table. I have to get back before he does," was Robert's whimsical way of saying he had some work to do for Blackett.

Shortly after Robert returned to Cambridge a visitor from the University of Göttingen arrived at the Cavendish Laboratory. Herr Professor Max Born's scientific reputation was well known, and Robert eagerly awaited the opportunity to meet the brilliant professor.

Born had joined the University of Göttingen in 1921. Known for his talent, tireless industry and passion for the new physics, Born had much in common with Oppenheimer. Their instant rapport was not surprising. But those who knew both Born and Oppenheimer think the two men had much more than physics in common. Born, like Oppenheimer, was a man of many interests and talents.

During Born's stay in Cambridge he and Robert worked together. Born later said, "Oppenheimer seemed to me right from the beginning a very gifted man." And before Born left he urged Robert to come to Göttingen, saying, "In Göttingen, you will find the most advanced scientific thinking in the world today."

It is not known whether Robert decided at that moment to go on to the University of Göttingen or whether he deliberated his future for some time before making up his mind. When he completed his work at Cavendish, he left for Germany.

After Cambridge, Robert might have been disappointed by the bleakness of Göttingen, in 1926. Only seven years earlier Germany had signed the Treaty of Versailles.

This Treaty not only humiliated her pride by a control of sovereign rights, but it also left the country with territorial losses, which caused diminishing food supplies and dangerous damage to industry. The country suffered an inflation that wiped out the economy. Striking examples of this surrounded Robert. The inflation had forced the government to issue vast amounts of paper money, the worth of which was less than the value of the paper.

One American scientist, also at Göttingen in 1926, commented, "It was a great place scientifically, but a dreadful place to live," while another American physicist remembers that the bottom of the Leine River Canal, which runs through Göttingen, was filled with worthless aluminum and iron coins.

Robert, along with several other foreign students, including E. U. Condon and Paul Dirac, roomed at the fine granite villa of Dr. Cario, whose son, Gunther, was also working toward a name in physics. Before the war, the Carios had been quite wealthy, but now they too felt the devastation of the post-war years in Germany, so much so that they had to take in "paying guests."

Max Born tells of an experience he had with Oppenheimer. "I used to tell my students that I am not very good at long calculations and always make mistakes. Once I wrote a paper which seemed to me important, and which contained rather lengthy and complicated calculations. I made these quite alone. To be on the safe side I gave them to Oppenheimer for checking. After a few days he came to me and said: 'They are perfectly correct. Have you really done this alone?' It was an impudence but I was not angry with him, but recognized his straightforward honesty."

Although the relationship between teacher and pupil was close at the Cavendish Laboratory, it did not compare with the comradeship found in Göttingen. Here the professors made no secret of their mistakes, and frequently voiced their doubts. They kept their students informed on their private correspondence with foreign colleagues, and also prompted them to seek out explanations wherever they could be found.

Each week in Room 204 of the Institute, Born held a "Seminar on Matter," and according to several of the men who attended these seminars, it became almost a tradition for Born, James Franck, or David Hilbert to open the session with a pretense of innocence: "Gentlemen, can anyone tell me, what exactly is an atom?" Each time the question was asked, the problem was tackled anew, and each time they searched for a different solution. If a student sought refuge in esoteric definitions or long mathematical equations, Hilbert would interrupt: "I can't understand. Will you please tell me again?" This question forced everyone to express himself as clearly and as simply as possible. But most of all, it forced the students to construct solid thoughts.

Robert never lacked a sense of humor and he often told stories on himself. One of his favorites was a conversation he had with Paul Dirac when they were both in Göttingen. One evening Dirac took Robert aside and said, "I don't understand you. In science we try to say things no one has ever said before, in a way that everyone can understand. But in poetry, you say things in such a way that nobody can understand."

In the spring of 1927 Robert Oppenheimer applied for permission to take the examination for a doctor's degree. He had labored over his doctor's thesis for several months, and after reading it Max Born said, "It is excellent," and proposed that the paper, *Zur Quantentheorie Kontinuierlicher Spektren,* be marked "with distinction." The thesis was considered a brilliant paper on quantum mechanics.

On the afternoon of May 11, 1927, Robert took his oral examination. He passed in all subjects, except in one area of chemistry, with "excellent" or "very good." After the examination a colleague asked physicist James Franck how it had gone. Franck is said to have replied, "I got out of there just in time. He was beginning to ask me questions."

At twenty-three, just two years after graduating from Harvard, Robert was now J Robert Oppenheimer, Ph.D. He stayed on for a short time, writing a paper in collaboration with Max Born. The paper, *Zur Quantentheorie der Moleküln,* was later incorporated in Born's "Selected Papers," published by the Göttingen Academy, and is still quoted in papers and textbooks today.

One of the last things Robert did before returning home was to give Dr. Max Born an old, valuable edition of Lagrange's *Mécanique Analytique.* Many years later Max Born would write Oppenheimer:

> "This (the book) has survived all upheavals: revolution, war, emigration, and return, and I am glad that it is still in my library, for it represents very well your attitude to science which comprehends it as a part of the general intellectual development in the course of human history."

6 ☙ A DUTCH NAME

IN LATE SUMMER OF 1927, ROBERT SET SAIL FOR THE UNITED States. His experience in Europe had stimulated his development. At Cambridge and at Göttingen, the opportunity to measure himself against the world's elite had proved to him that he could stand with the best. Besides becoming Dr. J Robert Oppenheimer, he had reached emotional and intellectual maturity.

Robert never forgot his years of inner conflict. Because of his own experience, he never failed to hear a youth asking, "Who am I?" He responded with characteristic willingness; he tried always to give sensible answers, even when the questions were odd and fleeting. Robert showed, with utmost clarity his willingness to help when he answered his sixteen-year-old brother's letter, in which Frank also asked that perennial question, "Who am I?"

"Dear Frank:

You make it rather hard for me to write to you by assuring me with such confidence that I shall be writing to someone I have never known. But it is not easy to believe that the Frank I knew is completely vanished; and I should be very, very sorry if that were so. It has always seemed to me one of the inordinate inadequacies of letters—of letters which are not to serve some specific purpose, but are more or less gratuitous—that they necessarily give a pretty partial account of the writer, an account, at once trivial and misleading. And for that reason I cannot be so desperate about our inability to keep flourishing a correspondence. The only letters which I can write with any conviction are technical ones, telling of physics, discursive and wholly ideational letters, love letters, and informative letters, which give geography and chronology and the major external data. It seems to me intrinsic to the act of living seriously that one should not be able to detach oneself enough to give a simple reflective account of what it is all about; the ability to do that comes only after the events are over, after one has ceased to be involved, when, that is, one is no longer the same person. . . . Nevertheless, I think that you do overestimate the inconstancy and incoherence of personal life; for I believe that throughout the variations—and they are wild enough, God knows—there is, there should be, and in mature people there comes more and more to be a certain unity, which makes it possible to recognize a man in his most diverse operations, a kind of specific personal stamp, which characterizes not so much the what as the how of a man's business. And this stamp is borne also by the letters, and is to be found, not in the contents of the letter, which may refer to a brief mood or a manic spell of action, but in the overtones of the attitude that the writer takes toward what he is writing. . . . And you must so excuse me for not sending you a character sketch, or asking you for one; neither of us, I think, could furnish one adequately. For purposes of recognition it will suffice for you to know that I am six feet tall, have black hair, blue eyes, and at present a split lip, and that I answer to the call of Robert."

The letter shows the finished product of two years in Europe. Robert Oppenheimer had found himself and much of that for which he had searched.

In Germany Robert had suffered from frequent colds that he attributed to damp weather and poorly heated buildings. He developed a chronic cough. Robert, himself, didn't help matters. He chain smoked, and kept an impossible schedule, often forgetting to eat or sleep. But with more important matters at hand, Robert ignored the cough, for the most part, thinking it would pass in time.

Word of Robert's brilliant performance in Göttingen had preceded him to the United States. Many university offers flew his way. He had refused three European offers: the Universities of Berlin, Leipzig, and the Sorbonne in Paris. Robert wanted to teach the new physics in his homeland. He had a total of ten offers, some from the best universities in the United States: Harvard, Princeton, Columbia, Chicago. He decided to postpone teaching for a year and accepted two National Research Council Fellowships—Harvard and California Institute of Technology.

Robert started the academic year of 1927–28 at Harvard. During this time, he submitted a poem that appeared in the June 1928 issue of the Harvard Miscellany called *Hound and Horn*.

CROSSING

It was evening when we came to the river
with a low moon over the desert
that we had lost in the mountains, forgotten,
what with the cold and the sweating
and the ranges barring the sky.
And when we found it again,
in the dry hills down by the river,
half withered, we had
the hot winds against us.

There were two palms by the landing;
the yuccas were flowering; there was
a light on the far shore, and tamarisks.
We waited a long time, in silence.
Then we heard the oars creaking
and afterwards, I remember,

the boatman called to us.
We did not look back at the mountains.

Using imagery to express his own dry, sterile intellectuality, Robert saw himself as a man caught in a web of his own making. In this poem, Robert marks the beginning of his swing from aloofness to awareness.

Upon completion of his work at Harvard, Robert went to the California Institute of Technology, or Cal Tech, as it is called. Cal Tech delighted Robert. Here he worked under Robert A. Millikan, who, for one of his many contributions to atomic physics, had received the Nobel Prize in physics (1923) for his work on the elementary charge of electricity and photoelectric phenomena.

While in Pasadena Robert decided that he wanted to teach at Cal Tech, then decided he could be useful to both Cal Tech and the University of California at Berkeley. The idea of concurrent appointments began with a letter from Elmer E. Hall, chairman of the physics department at Berkeley.

Hall, on March 5, 1928, had written Robert offering him an assistant professorship at the yearly rate of $3,000. Hall's offer, which bypassed the first level of the salary scale, is said to have caused some resentment among the older faculty members who grumbled, saying, the university now valued young men more highly than the older, more experienced teachers. While this statement was true, it must be remembered that these men were out seeking knowledge and understanding of the new physics. Another factor not considered was the practice of the university to obtain letters of recommendation before making an offer of employment to a professor. One letter, in particular, carried considerable weight in the university's decision to make an offer to J Robert Oppenheimer. James Franck, who had taught Robert in Göttingen, wrote that he considered Robert Oppenheimer the most promising young physicist in America.

Robert answered Professor Hall's letter on March 10.

While accepting the position, Robert asked that the appointment be postponed for a year. "I have decided to go abroad again to study a little in Europe," wrote Robert. "I feel that I, myself, am not yet sufficiently well trained to be of much use to others."

Arrangements were made. Robert accepted concurrent appointments at both Cal Tech and the University of California for the academic year 1929–1930. For the fall semester, Robert would belong to Berkeley; for the winter and spring quarters, Cal Tech would claim him. But Dr. Oppenheimer's teaching career lay in the future. How could he teach when he still considered himself a student? He had been offered an International Education Board Fellowship, and as he said in his letter to Chairman Hall, he wanted to study abroad.

Before going on to New York, Robert made a stop in New Mexico. But this time, his visit was for more than just pleasure. Katherine Page had told him about the Harvey Ranch, of one hundred and sixty acres that might be available. Robert liked the place immediately and decided to rent it temporarily. All the arrangements would be taken care of and the ranch would be Robert's and Frank's when Robert returned from Europe next year. "Hot dog!" said Robert expressing his delight.

Katherine Page corrected him. "No, Perro Caliente!"

"Of course." Robert understood. "Hot dog in Spanish."

The ranch was named.

Frank Oppenheimer, who had been at a summer camp in Colorado, met Robert in New Mexico toward the end of summer. He approved his brother's choice, and when they left for the East, it was with great anticipation of the following summer.

Twenty-five year old Oppenheimer set sail for Europe. His first stop was the University of Leiden in the Netherlands. At first he haunted the university library, burying himself in quantum physics. The Robert Oppenheimer of two years earlier might have continued to devote himself to his work. But this was the new Robert in Leiden. Allowing himself time away from his work, he strolled along the cobblestone streets, examined the dikes, and, armed with a Dutch dictionary, frequently stopped and chatted with the townspeople.

At the university both students and faculty were taken with his personal charm as well as with his ability. They expressed their fondness by calling him "Opje." The Dutch nickname would become "Oppie" in America, but it would be with pleasant memories that Robert would remember the Dutch scholars and the significance of "Opje."

After completing his work in Leiden, Robert moved on to Zurich, Switzerland, where he also held an International Education Board Fellowship, this time at the Federal Institute of Technology. Here he met Wolfgang Pauli and welcomed the opportunity to work with the great physicist. Of Pauli, Robert often said, "He was such a good physicist that things broke down or blew up when he merely walked into a laboratory." Because of his own ineptitude in the lab, Robert no doubt found this encouraging.

Working with Pauli in Zurich was another promising young physicist named Felix Bloch, whose work in nuclear physics later earned him a Nobel Prize. Bloch, a native of Zurich, showed Robert the sights, introduced him to the fine Swiss wines, and acquainted him with the history of Switzerland. Recalls Bloch, "What first impressed me about Oppenheimer was the breadth of his interests. He was not a man one could exhaust with a simple formula."

It seems that wherever Robert went he took a part of home with him. Bloch remembers the time he first visited Robert's apartment in Zurich. "Oppenheimer had many things he had brought with him from New Mexico. I was particularly impressed by the beautiful Navajo rug he had on his sofa." Bloch, who had never been in the United States, asked Robert to tell him about his country. Had Bloch not had a genuine interest in knowing more about the United States, he might easily have regretted his request, for given such an opportunity, Robert's enthusiasm ran rampant. Laughing, Bloch recalled, "There was no mistaking the intensity of Oppenheimer's affection for his country. His attachment was most apparent."

The season wore on; Oppenheimer's stay in beautiful Zurich ended. The time had come to return to the United States. Oppenheimer said goodby to Bloch. Neither of the men knew whether they would meet again. But as fate would have it Bloch would plant permanent roots in Oppenheimer's country in the spring of 1934; and the men were destined to meet again in California.

7 ⊗ PERRO CALIENTE

"IN THE SPRING OF 1929," ROBERT WROTE LATER, "I RETURNED
to the United States. I was homesick for this country, and in fact
I did not leave it again for nineteen years. I had learned a great
deal in my student days about the new physics; I wanted to pursue this myself, to explain it, and to foster its cultivation . . . ."

Although preoccupied with quantum physics and the birth
of his teaching career, Robert's health, at this point, must have
caused him some concern. His cough had hung on for two years,
growing steadily worse. His lean frame now looked gaunt. He
had difficulty sleeping. Doctors feared tuberculosis. They advised him to go West.

Doctors' orders fit perfectly with Robert's plans. He had
every intention of returning to New Mexico. All the arrangements had been completed the summer before, when he had
leased the Harvey Ranch, or as it was now known, Perro
Caliente.

Frank Oppenheimer, who had been in Colorado, went directly to New Mexico, arriving before his brother. Books, Coleman lanterns, and the usual supplies needed for rugged living, plus a few bottles of kirschwasser, the fragrant, colorless brandy distilled from the fermented juice of black morello cherries for which Robert had developed a taste while in Europe, had already been sent out to the ranch.

A short time later, Robert arrived in Santa Fe. He made one purchase, a modified Stetson; then went on to the Page Ranch where he visited with Katherine Page and picked up "Blue," the saddle horse she had offered to loan him for the summer.

To Robert, Perro Caliente was something found only in dreams. He had his books, a horse, and all the solitude he wanted. Most of the daylight hours were spent riding. He and Frank explored the peaks and valleys, and Frank recalls that it was quite common for them to ride as much as a thousand miles in one summer.

As always, the liveliness of Robert's mind prevented complete relaxation. After a tiring day of hiking or riding, Robert would sit up reading or writing by the light of a Coleman lantern. He kept up with the latest developments in quantum physics and he wrote to colleagues, telling them of his latest thoughts on the subject.

He had often said, and would continue to say, that he longed for a leisurely life. He now had freedom from studies and had not yet entered into the demands of academic life. Why then did he not take advantage of this brief pause?

Examined casually, his words and actions appear contradictory. But part of the contradiction is removed, or at least accounted for, when we realize that Oppenheimer, all of his life, was plagued by the desire to attain more than ordinary mastery of his field. He suffered from the need to find answers to unsolved problems; and he felt the urgency of developing new insights. He had a strong sense of what needed to be done and he knew that he had the cerebral capacity and the appropriate means of expression essential for the advancement of quantum physics. His perennial restlessness would often be mistakenly interpreted as discontent. Robert was no more able to escape the wholeness of motive in his nature—the inordinate appetite for discovery—than were other geniuses.

Robert Oppenheimer leaned toward the metaphysical in the sense that he believed in the free use of imagination and saw the value of imagination. He also found satisfaction in the writings of the 17th century metaphysical poets: Donne, Herbert, Crashaw, and Marvell. His attraction to the metaphysical is not difficult to understand. He could not find a logical reason for his restlessness, nor could he explain the spontaneous activity of his mind, the inspirations that seemed to appear from nowhere.

Robert's willingness to step beyond into the less understood world of metaphysics was just one of the many ways in which he departed from the customary. He listened to the voice of eccentricity—eccentricity in himself and in the world around him.

Perro Caliente offered Robert the leisurely life and it also produced profound effects on his life. Here he first said, in a letter to a friend, "My two great loves are physics and New Mexico. It's a pity they can't be combined." The two brothers, now with similar interests, got to know and respect each other as individuals, on an intellectual basis. Robert later said, "There was a strong bond of affection between us"; and Frank was to voice almost identical words.

As summer wore on, Robert became a familiar figure on the road to Cowles, the post office nearest to Perro Caliente. His health improved and he even gained weight. His physical ruggedness resulted in part from his wood-chopping chores. "Watching Robert was entertaining," Frank Oppenheimer remembers. "He'd chase the wood down the road."

Robert no doubt had mixed feelings when he left Perro Caliente. The summer had been one of the best in his life; he hated to leave the land and the solitude he loved. Yet, he looked forward to his first semester as a teacher. There was so much he had to say about the new physics. He had spent the summer thinking about all he had learned during his student days. Now he longed to share with other eager minds all that he knew, all that he thought. He wanted to father a new breed of physicists in the United States, to help make his country the center of the new physics.

Robert planned on stopping in Pasadena before driving up the California coast to Berkeley. When he finally arrived in Pasadena, he had not shaved or washed for several days, and according to a colleague, "looked more like a tramp than a college professor." Undaunted, he walked into the Norman Bridge Laboratory, flashed a big smile, and announced, "I'm Oppenheimer."

II

THE
TEACHER
SCIENTIST
(1929-1942)

8 ⟡ THE NEW FACE
OF PHYSICS

THE YEARS 1925 TO 1929 HAD BROUGHT SEVERAL NEW DEVELOP-
ments to the quantum theory: the Schrödinger equation, the
Dirac equation, field theory, and quantum electrodynamics.
That these developments were so completely European, illus-
trates how asleep American theoretical physics had remained.

Then in 1929 American physics wakened and lunged forward. The old classical physics had been replaced by a new,
burgeoning, quantum physics. Robert Oppenheimer was one of
the men who led this forward movement of American quantum
physics. In the three years between 1926 and 1929 he published
sixteen papers dealing with quantum theory. But so prolific
was he with both ideas and words that by 1945 he had published
an astonishing number of technical papers—sixty-six—each
of which presented the most advanced thinking and work in
the field of quantum physics.

Robert's first teaching assignment at Berkeley was a graduate course in quantum mechanics. He also held a seminar. But almost as soon as he began his career, his students complained that he progressed so rapidly that they could not keep up with his lectures. Then, a few weeks later, Oppenheimer presented the chairman of the physics department with the opposite problem. "I'm going so slowly," he complained in deep discouragement, "that I'm not getting anywhere."

"This was my first intimation of the speed at which Oppenheimer's mind worked," recalls Professor Emeritus Raymond Birge, the retired chairman of the Berkeley physics department. Professor Birge went on to say, "Oppenheimer is definitely the greatest genius I have known intimately."

But Robert's "genius" did not encompass social awareness. He remained almost totally oblivious to the social and economic events taking place in the United States. He learned of the October 29 market crash long after it occurred and when he did learn of it, although he realized that the United States faced grave economic problems, he left concern to the men who ran the country.

Robert divorced himself not only from the contemporary scene but from the world view as well. The crash, the Depression, the heated conflict between labor unions and industry, the rise of Facism in Europe, or the hungry eye of Communism on America all meant little to Robert. His interests lay elsewhere, and this he admits himself: "I was interested in man and his experience; I was deeply interested in *my* science; but I had no understanding of the relations of man to his society." And thus his interests remained for the next seven years.

When the Berkeley semester ended, Robert left for Cal Tech to teach the spring quarter. Here his eagerness to explain and foster the new physics met a receptive audience. Members of the faculty flocked into the room where he was scheduled to deliver his first lecture. Students cut classes to come and sit in, and instead of finding a handful of graduate students, Robert walked into a room filled beyond capacity.

Impressed by the turnout and sure that each person in the room shared his enthusiasm, Robert began his lecture. He spoke rapidly, using long, poetic phrases to explain his point. His hand braced his chin or covered his lips as he spoke. Then, as his thought changed he whirled toward the blackboard and dashed off a few equations. He threw out dozens of quotes from the greatest minds in science. He chain-smoked. He played on words, used complicated puns and unusual words with abstruse meanings, and spoke in a soft, low voice that grew even lower when he wanted to emphasize a point.

The onlookers sat silent—hypnotized. Suddenly his lean six-foot frame seemed to grow as he spoke. It was as though his body took on the largeness of his mind, and he was no longer frail to the point of transparency. In spite of his extreme youth he appeared ageless.

His face revealed a mind openly at work. From it shone a strange beauty—the beauty of intensity, of awareness, of sensitivity, of a transcending intelligence.

The lecture ended. The room emptied. Only Professor Richard Tolman remained. Robert looked at Tolman, eagerly awaiting his comments. What must he have felt when at last Tolman said, "Well, Robert, that was beautiful, but I didn't understand a damn word."

So anxious was Robert to share his knowledge with others that he hadn't realized that no one had understood him. Why were they so attentive? Professor Oppenheimer's lecture was filled with action and drama. The flow of his voice and the feeling in his beautifully chosen words held his audience spellbound. They had never heard anyone lecture with such dramatic sincerity.

But Robert's inability to reach his students was not his only failing as a teacher. His snapping sarcasms stung more than one person. He was quick, impatient, and intolerant of shoddy and fuzzy thinking. Also, he had the habit of giving an answer before a student had finished asking a question.

Glenn Seaborg, Chairman of the United States Atomic Energy Commission, said, remembering his student days at Berkeley, "I imagine I had one difficulty with Oppie that was common to all who sought his advice, that is, facing his tendency to answer your question even before you had fully stated it." Seaborg goes on to tell how he took great pains in formulating his questions to Oppenheimer, putting the main thrust of his thoughts as early as possible into every sentence.

In his early days of teaching, Robert is reputed to have "terrorized" his students. One student remembers how Oppenheimer "could be, and often was, a rough person to have in the audience when giving a lecture. Frequently he'd take the speaker apart, verbally." Robert is reported to have interrupted many a lecturer with caustic comments like, "Oh, come now! We all know that. Let's get on with it," or "That is totally incorrect and you should know better."

"To say that Oppenheimer didn't suffer fools gladly," another ex-student quipped, "is an understatement!"

Robert Christy, who received his Ph.D. under Oppenheimer, said, "Oppie had a strong view of physics, of how the subject should be presented, of how the work should be done. He had exceedingly high standards and he imposed these standards on others."

But gradually and painfully, coached by his colleagues, and profiting from his errors, Robert made an effort to be more easily understood by using shorter, less obscure words, and to save his sarcasms for showoffs.

Soon Robert became a teacher who was able to pass on the same sense of challenge he felt. Robert Serber, a distinguished high energy physicist who spent his National Research Fellowship under Oppenheimer, tells of the more experienced teacher

✿ *Dr. J Robert Oppenheimer confers with former student,*
Dr. Robert Serber

U.S. INFORMATION AGENCY

he knew. Oppenheimer's "course was an inspirational as well as an educational achievement. He transmitted to his students a feeling of the beauty of the logical structure of physics and an excitement about the development of physics. Almost everyone listened to the course more than once: Oppie occasionally had difficulty dissuading students from coming for a third or fourth time."

Never giving his students easy surface answers, Robert trained them to appreciate and work on deep problems. Just as Max Born and James Franck in Göttingen had urged him to express himself clearly and simply, and just as they had forced their students to construct solid thoughts, so did Robert train his students; and he achieved success. So well did he challenge their thinking and spark their imaginations that his classrooms were soon jammed with arguing, questioning students. Oppenheimer now fathered his own tense breed of physicists in California, just as he had once been fathered in Göttingen.

"Oppie's way of working with his research students was also original," writes Robert Serber. "His group consisted of eight or ten graduate students and about a half dozen post-doctoral fellows. He met the group once a day in his office. A little before the appointed time the members straggled in and disposed themselves on the tables and about the walls. Oppie came in and discussed, with one after another, the status of the student's research problem, while the others listened and offered comments. All were exposed to a broad range of topics. Oppen-heimer was interested in everything; one subject after another was introduced and coexisted with all the others. In an after-noon they might discuss electrodynamics, cosmic rays, astro-physics and nuclear physics."

To his students, Robert became both master and model. In Berkeley he was called "Oppie" but in Pasadena, from the mo-ment he walked onto the Cal Tech campus, he, as if magically, "metamorphosed into Robert." When he ended a course in

Berkeley, many of his students followed him to Cal Tech. Along the way he'd stop for roadside seminars. The students who followed Robert from campus to campus became known as "Oppenheimer's satellites."

So greatly did his students admire him that they began to imitate their master's mannerisms. "They scribbled furiously on the blackboard, talked in soft, deep tones." They held their hands in front of their lips; they coughed slightly, and paused significantly between sentences. "Some even took up chain-smoking and blue shirts!"

Robert, a confirmed smoker, had a habit of clicking open his lighter whenever anyone took out a cigarette or a pipe. Soon "his students could be recognized from afar in the campus cafeterias of Berkeley and Pasadena by their custom of darting about like marionettes on invisible strings, with tiny flames between their fingers."

Along with adopting Oppenheimer's physical mannerisms, his students also acquired his intolerance for shoddy and fuzzy thinking, his intuitive grasp of difficulties, his mathematical precision of speech.

"I guess we revered the man as much as we venerated the scientist," said an ex-Oppenheimer pupil.

Robert's magnetic personality doubtless accounted for a good part of his unique power as a teacher. Many a person has tried to explain Oppenheimer's unusual ability to influence. What special personal quality did he have that allowed him to command, influence, to compel such veneration?

Philosopher Will Dennes who for many years knew Oppenheimer both as a colleague and a personal friend answers the question with one word: *"Charisma."*

In theology the word is defined as a divinely conferred gift or power. In the psychological and philosophical sense the word charisma means a special personal quality that gives an individual influence, or authority, over a large number of people.

9 ⊚ LIVING LEGEND

SEPTEMBER, 1931—ROBERT OPPENHEIMER WAS PROMOTED TO Associate Professor at the University of California in Berkeley, but it was another three years before he reached the same level at the California Institute of Technology in Pasadena.

In the two years he had been teaching theoretical physics, Robert had laid the foundation for the great school of physics he was creating. With the growth of Robert Oppenheimer's school of modern physics and Ernest Lawrence's invention of the cyclotron both taking place in Berkeley, the University was destined to become one of the leading centers of nuclear physics.

Within a few weeks of the new semester Robert received a wire from his father which pushed all thoughts of physics to the background.

October 6, 1931

"Mother critically ill. Not expected to live . . ."

Robert immediately applied for a leave of absence. That night he flew to New York.

A friend who saw Robert shortly after he had received the wire remembers the agony on his face. "He had a terribly desolate look. 'My mother's dying. My mother's dying,' he repeated again and again. I then realized how very close he and his mother must have been."

Ella Friedman Oppenheimer died of leukemia a few days later. For the first time in his life, twenty-five year old Robert knew personal loss. He grieved deeply.

On October 17 Robert returned to his job at Berkeley, leaving his grief-stricken father behind. But Ella's death would bring the father and son closer together. "After my mother's death," wrote Robert, "my father came often, mostly in Berkeley, to visit me; and we had an intimate and close association until his death."

Robert spent a part of every summer at Perro Caliente. Many guests visited the ranch, and from these visits have originated many tales still told today. Always long and lean, Robert had a small appetite. He preferred to nibble rather than feast on a large meal. Unfortunately, it never occurred to him that not all his guests liked to eat as he did and many of them had hearty appetites. One starving ranch guest, when hearing Robert was riding into town for supplies, offered to go along. The famished young visitor watched Robert load up on his usual tid-bits: canned artichoke hearts, smoked oysters, pickled string beans, and finally decided that if he didn't suggest some more substantial foods he'd not have the strength to return to California. "Don't you think we should get some potatoes?" he asked hopefully.

Robert paused, thought for a moment, then said, "That's a splendid idea. Let's get *a pound*."

Perhaps it was because of similar experiences that past visitors to the ranch, when hearing that someone was invited for the first time, would say, "You'll have a wonderful time, but you'd better bring your own food."

Robert's relations with his students were not confined to the classroom or summers at Perro Caliente. His hospitality extended to the campus. Often, when he and his students worked late, he'd invite them home with him. Once there he'd prepare a supper of "eggs a la Oppie" or some other hot, spicy Mexican dish on which he prided himself as a chef. With this he'd serve red wine and tossed salad. Writes Robert Serber, "When Oppie was supplying the food, the novices suffered from the hot chili that social conduct required them to eat."

In the spring of 1934, Felix Bloch, whom Robert had met and come to know in Zurich, Switzerland, came to the United States. Bloch took out citizenship and accepted a teaching position at Stanford University in Palo Alto, California. The distance between Stanford and Berkeley is not great, but the two cities are separated by the San Francisco Bay.

Oppenheimer and Bloch immediately set up weekly joint seminars with their students. One week Bloch and his group traveled to Berkeley, the next, Oppenheimer and his "satellites" went to Stanford. After these seminars, Robert frequently treated the entire group to dinner in San Francisco.

Says Bob Serber, "These were Depression days when students were poor. The world of good food and good wines and gracious living was far from the experience of many. . . . Oppie introduced us to an unfamiliar way of life." Then Serber adds, "We acquired something of his tastes."

But all of Robert's social activities were not with his students. Stories of his difficulties with girls are still told around the Berkeley and Pasadena campuses. On one occasion Robert took a date up to Grizzly Peak, a hill overlooking Berkeley. Then he was struck with a solution to the problem he had been pondering all day. He excused himself, got out of the car, and started walking. But, as the story goes, Robert became so involved in his mental problem that he continued walking. He walked all the way back home, then, having concluded his mental excursion, went to bed. Apparently the girl had to be rescued by the police and the morning's paper carried the story under a headline which read:

ABSENT MINDED PROFESSOR
FORGETS DATE ON HILL

In Berkeley Robert met Sanskrit scholar Arthur Ryder. At once the two men became friends and Ryder taught Robert to read Sanskrit, the ancient language of the Hindus. It didn't take Robert long to master Sanskrit well enough to read the *Bagavad-Gita,* or "The Lord's Song." Of the *Gita,* Robert said, "It is the most beautiful philosophical song existing in any known tongue."

As a token of their friendship, Ryder presented Robert with a pink covered copy of the holy book. Robert so cherished the gift, that from that day on, it held a place of honor in his library. Robert thought the *Bhagavad-Gita* so beautiful that he often gave friends translated copies as gifts.

Although unknown to the general public, by 1935 J Robert Oppenheimer had earned a glowing international reputation among scientists. A growing number of advanced students of the highest caliber came from all over the United States to work under his guidance. His lectures remained unsurpassed not only in delivery, but also in content—the most advanced work in the field of theoretical physics. His lectures were so well prepared that Miss Rebecca Young, secretary of the Berkeley physics department, mimeographed them and sold them to the students who then used them as textbooks. During the depression years the universities lacked many of the necessary funds taken for granted today. The physics department never had sufficient funds in the petty cash box. The money Miss Young made from Oppenheimer's lectures was put into this fund.

A colleague, who has copies of Oppenheimer's lectures and

who still refers to them, commented, "Had Oppenheimer gone one step further and compiled his lectures and papers, his work would have made one of the finest textbooks on quantum physics ever written."

10 ❧ FROM THE LEFT

IN 1936 ROBERT'S INTERESTS BEGAN TO CHANGE. "TO MANY OF my friends, my indifference to contemporary affairs seemed bizarre, and they often chided me with being too much of a highbrow," Robert wrote later.

What triggered Robert's belated social awareness? He said, "I had a smoldering fury about the treatment of Jews in Germany." Many of his relatives still lived in Germany under the totalitarian dictatorship. The Jews were deprived of virtually all rights and were subjected to intensive persecution. Julius Oppenheimer made a trip to Europe, trying to arrange for his sister Selma to come to the United States. But Selma died before plans were consummated. Julius' youngest sister, Hedwig, had spent many summers in New York with the Oppenheimers, and after her husband's death, arrangements were made for her, her son, and his family to leave Germany to live in the United States. Hedwig planned to live with Julius, but in 1937, as she was crossing the Atlantic, Julius Oppenheimer died of a heart attack.

His father's death came as a severe blow to Robert. Now he had lost both of his parents. Robert picked up where Julius left off. He carried out the rest of the arrangements, and his Aunt Hedwig and her son, a doctor, and his family, settled in Berkeley.

The Depression provided the second factor in Robert's social awakening. He saw how it affected his students. Without money many could not continue their education. Frequently Robert would give them money to help them out. Others, fortunate enough to have fellowships, found that when they completed their university work, they could not find positions.

Through the students, said Robert, "I began to understand how deeply political and economic events could affect men's lives. I began to feel the need to participate more fully in the life of the community."

From the Depression, the spread of Fascism and Nazism and the threat of war, a mood of social protest swept the United States. Robert Oppenheimer awakened to the mood later than most. He saw the plight of the California migratory farm workers. He recognized the goals of the struggling labor unions. He witnessed bright, promising students dropping out of school because they lacked funds necessary to continue. He heard of private schools collapsing and became discouraged by the drastic economies that crippled education by the discharging of teachers and the overcrowding of classrooms. To Robert Oppenheimer, who believed that education was an integral part of the social order, educational growth was being turned back. His fury mounted. He had to do something.

He listened to the words of philosopher John Dewey and the words made sense. Oppenheimer, like Dewey, relied on social intelligence based on scientific procedures to solve the problem of adjustment to a changing industrial environment. Oppenheimer might have been called a pragmatist for he too believed in seeking solutions by continuous experiment within the peaceful framework of discussion, education, and social planning. He believed in wiping out educational inequalities between races and classes, and in strengthening the educational responsibilities of teachers in decisive educational aims and methods. He saw that these and other changes would equip the individual to advance both himself and society.

In 1919 the American Communist Party was formed, but for the first fifteen years of its existence, its influence was insignificant. How then, during the thirties, did this small, ineffectual sect, controlled from Russia, attract so many well-known intellectuals? The answer is found in a strange mixture of historical, political, and psychological happenings that began at the end of the 1920's.

As the Depression in the United States deepened, as Fascism and Nazism grew in power, as Franklin D. Roosevelt and his New Deal took the reins of American government and civil war broke out in Spain, the Soviet Union emerged as the "champion of peace." In 1935 the Seventh Congress of the Communist International (Comintern) announced a new Communist line which was to suspend the class struggle against the bourgeois parties and moderate socalists (whom they had formerly called "social fascists") and promote class collaboration with the middle-class groups that opposed Fascism. Following the new orders from Russia, the American Communist Party changed its tune. Communism, it said, was really "Twentieth Century Americanism."

After their original opposition to Roosevelt, the American Communist Party began to support him. The Party criticized the D.A.R. for its failure to celebrate the 162nd anniversary of Paul Revere's ride. It paraded on Broadway in New York with a sign reading "The D.A.R. Forgets, but the Y.C.L. (Young Communist League) Remembers." Front organizations sprang up and one, the American League for Peace and Democracy, brought many non-Communists to the Popular Front movement—a few congressmen, a Grand Exalted Ruler of the Elks, leaders of certain labor unions, and even religious groups. People began to think of Communists as dedicated "progressives in a hurry." Also, through the Popular Front, the Communist Party penetrated or controlled several of the CIO unions.

Robert Oppenheimer was not an isolated case. Many American intellectuals descended their "ivory towers" to find their country in misery and strife. They, too, rebelled, and in so doing were easy prey for the Communists. Robert joined the rebellion in what he thought were movements of humanitarian objectives, just as many other intellectuals did. In less than twenty years many of these men and women would pay severely for their naïveté.

During this same period, friends introduced Robert to Jean Tatlock, the daughter of a noted English professor at Berkeley. Jean, who was also a Ph.D. and a member of the American Communist Party, and Robert grew close. Their friendship lasted for three years.

Robert's relationship with Jean Tatlock delighted his friends and associates. Not only was she a beautiful, highly intelligent and well-educated woman, but she was, according to a friend, "worthy of Robert in every way. They had much in common."

But of his leftwing associations, Robert wrote, "I should not give the impression that it was wholly because of Jean Tatlock that I made leftwing friends . . . I liked the new sense of companionship, and at the time felt that I was coming to be a part of the life of my time and country." Robert also said, "She told me of her Communist Party memberships; they were on again, off again affairs, and never seemed to provide for her what she was seeking. I do not believe her interests were really political. She loved this country and its people and its life."

Those who knew Jean Tatlock agree with Oppenheimer.

They found her to be a "generous but troubled girl, whose sensitive nature, which was much like Robert's, made it easy for the Communists to exploit her emotionalism."

During the thirties Communism appealed to the intellectuals because it supported humanitarian causes but many of these causes were not Communist. The Communist Party presented itself as an ideal form of society which embraced love for mankind. Communism particularly attracted the young scientists "because it was presented as a completely logical, scientific organization of government and society." And in Robert's case, "love of mankind and humanitarian causes" were all an intricate part of his early "Ethical" training.

In the United States, those liberals who were sympathetic to the Communist cause—the love of mankind and the assortment of humanitarian causes—but who never took that fatal step, joining the Party—were known as fellow travelers. In this sense, Robert Oppenheimer was a fellow traveler.

In 1937 Robert met another fellow traveler, Haakon Chevalier. A professor of French at Berkeley, Chevalier was known to be "very much a Bohemian," although many people also considered Oppenheimer "Bohemian." The two men became fast friends, and, although there are those who feel that Chevalier used his friendship with Oppenheimer to further his own ends, the general picture seems to be one of an association that was good for both men, at least for a time.

Both Chevalier and Oppenheimer worked hard to establish the Teachers Union, Local 349. Robert contributed to the strike fund during one of the major strikes of Harry Bridges' union. He subscribed to *People's World,* a Communist newspaper; and he contributed to the various committees and organizations intended to help the Spanish Loyalist cause. Like many non-Communists and fellow travelers, he took part in or contributed to various other organizations. He held membership in the western council of the Consumer's Union, and the American Committee for Democracy and Intellectual Freedom, which at that time stood as a protest against the treatment of intellectuals and professionals in Germany.

But Robert's greatest involvement seems to have been in connection with the war in Spain. He said, "The defeat of the Loyalists caused me great sorrow." Even after the Spanish Civil War, he continued to make contributions through Communist channels to Spanish relief funds and also contributed to the organization of migratory farm labor in the California valleys. Then, showing his complete naïveté, Robert said, "I doubt that it occurred to me that the contributions might be directed to other purposes than those I had intended, or that such purposes might be evil."

Opinions of Robert's naïveté differ, but in general, the majority of the people who knew Oppenheimer well, even intimately, claim that he was indeed naïve enough never to have questioned the destination of his donations. Having come into a considerable inheritance after his father's death, he felt it was his moral duty to assist those in need. Also Robert was trusting. To him, it would not have been honorable to deceive anyone.

Just as the Depression pushed many men of sensibility and intelligence leftward, so the election of Franklin D. Roosevelt helped erase the isolation of the liberals. Roosevelt's election signaled the intellectuals' gradual rise to positions of influence. Although the vast majority of the university men did not go to work for the government, everybody knew someone who was connected with it. Also with Roosevelt's recognition of the Soviet Union in 1933, the leftwing liberals felt they were all a part of the same spectrum. They asked, "Was not the U.S.S.R. an experimental society just like America's New Deal?" Certainly both countries were moving toward socialism.

But was it only the Depression, the election of Roosevelt, the New Deal programs, and American recognition of Russia that gave the Popular Front its advantage? Many historians think not. The main issue that gave the Communists their long-awaited opportunity to move into power in the United States was the rise of Fascism. Fascism, if successful, affected everyone. To fight Fascism was to fight for one's own survival. Many people felt that their support of Communism was merely a means of fighting Fascism and war.

The Spanish Civil War dramatized the anti-Fascist struggle. It showed a triangular tragedy: a violent assault on the weak, aided by Italy and Germany; the shortsighted reaction of Britain and France, which was in effect sanctioned by America's silence; and the appearance of help from the Spanish Communists, foreign Communists, and non-Communists to the Loyalist cause in Spain.

In an atmosphere such as the Spanish Loyalist tragedy, it was easy for the Communists to play on the emotions of the liberal Americans. While awaiting their opportunity, they had had fifteen years of tough organization training from their Russian masters.

For some of the intellectuals, it was not until 1941, when the Nazis attacked Russia and they learned of the Hitler-Stalin non-aggression pact of 1939, that they realized how they had been used, manipulated, exploited. Other liberals broke with the Party because of thoroughly indigenous errors: a shallowness of thought, a rigidity of doctrine, and a too narrow sense of humanity.

Robert Oppenheimer's early doubts about the Communist Party were reinforced when, in 1938, he met three physicists who had lived in Russia during the thirties. Victor Weisskopf became a good friend and he related all he had seen happening in Russia. Wrote Oppenheimer, what he "reported seemed so solid, so unfanatical, so true, that it made a great impression; and it represented Russia . . . as a land of purge and terror, of ludicrously bad management and of a long-suffering people." Oppenheimer was not to be taken in again.

11 ❧ FISSION, FASCISM, FUSION

FROM 1929 TO 1939 AMERICANS HAD BEEN SO OCCUPIED WITH problems growing out of the Depression, that in comparison they gave scant attention to the rising crisis abroad. Now reviewed in retrospect, the events of the previous ten years took on a new perspective, and the whole frightening world panorama loomed before their eyes.

In 1930, only one year after Robert had left Europe, the grating notes of Nazi unrest echoed louder and louder. Even calm, peaceful Göttingen stirred when the leading newspaper, the *Göttinger Tageblatt,* praised Hitler as a "redeemer." Some students of the Second Physics and Mathematical Institutes discreetly circulated anti-Semitic literature and slandered Jewish undergraduates who had come from Poland or Hungary to study in Germany. They called Einstein's theory of relativity a "Jewish world-bluff." Yet young scientists of Jewish extraction continued to make notable contributions in quantum mechanics at Göttingen, Hamburg, and Berlin.

Gone was the complacency of the twenties, and unrest spread. Turbulence typified the times. Political assassinations became commonplace in Germany. Rioting broke out in Cuba and Spain; the Fascists blustered in Italy; and in the United States the Depression deepened. Neighborhood soup kitchens opened to feed the hungry. Christmas shoppers passed jobless shivering men selling apples on street corners.

In 1932 few people noticed a back-page article announcing that Sir James Chadwick, a British scientist, had discovered the neutron. Certainly issues like Japanese aggression, Hitler's gain in power, and the end of Prohibition, demanded more attention than the discovery of a new sub-atomic particle.

While the year 1939 marked the beginning of World War II, the deepest change in the character of science occurred. On January 16, 1939, the distinguished Danish theoretical physicist Niels Bohr arrived in New York almost unnoticed. Dr. Bohr was disturbed by the Nazi movements in Europe, and by a recent scientific discovery—and its implications.

Late in 1938 Otto Hahn and Fritz Strassmann, working at the Kaiser Wilhelm Institute for Chemistry in Berlin, had discovered a radioactive barium isotope resulting from their experiment: they had been bombarding uranium with neutrons. Hahn immediately recognized the significance of this discovery and sent his findings to Lise Meitner, an Austrian colleague who had fled Germany because of her Jewish heritage. Fraulein Meitner and her nephew, Otto Frisch, concluded that the presence of barium meant that a new type of atomic, or nuclear, reaction had taken place—Fission. They went at once to Copenhagen where they advanced the theory to Niels Bohr.

The developments leading up to the discovery of fission took more than forty years of dedicated hard work by some of the world's greatest scientists. A few of the many men involved were: J. J. Thompson, who discovered the electron in 1897; Lord Ernest Rutherford, who prepared a model of the nuclear atom in 1911; and Niels Bohr, who created the theoretical model of the atom (with its nucleus surrounded by orbiting electrons). In the general principles of the quantitative theory of atomic structure, the two central ideas of modern physics—Einstein's theory of relativity and Planck's quantum theory—played a decisive role. The work of the twenties opened new horizons of thinking, and provided the power and understanding for the work of the thirties—work by Anderson, Bothe and Becker, Chadwick, Fermi, Lawrence, Yukawa, Oliphant, Pauli, and many more. All these men contributed to the opening chapter of the Atomic Era.

Upon his arrival in the United States, Bohr went at once to Princeton, New Jersey, where he spent several months at the Institute for Advanced Study. Word of the discovery spread. Physicists from all over the country sought more information on the discovery. Isidor I. Rabi, at Princeton on sabbatical leave, rushed back to Columbia University the next morning to talk with Enrico Fermi. On January 26, Bohr and Fermi opened the Fifth Washington Conference on Theoretical Physics with a discussion of the exciting developments abroad. Press reports flashed to centers of physics research throughout the United States. Soon American scientists had the full story, for the *Physical Review* of February 15 carried an authoritative account by Bohr.

From the scientific standpoint the discovery of nuclear fission was stimulating because it pointed to the possibility of a self-sustaining chain reaction. Physicists thought it highly probable that fission released secondary neutrons. This meant that it might be possible to split other uranium nuclei, which in turn would liberate neutrons, and generate huge amounts of energy. If the process could be controlled, a new source of heat and power would be available. But if it were allowed to progress unchecked, an explosive of tremendous force might result.

Shortly after Bohr's arrival in the United States, Robert

Oppenheimer received word of the discovery. He called Felix Bloch at Stanford that very day. "You must come to Berkeley immediately," Robert told Bloch. "There is something of the utmost importance I must show you."

"There was a note of urgency in his voice," recalls Bloch, "one I don't recall ever having heard in Oppenheimer before."

Bloch left at once. When he arrived at Oppenheimer's office, he remembers Robert's opening words, "They have discovered fission."

Glenn Seaborg attended Oppenheimer's seminar when the new results of Otto Hahn and Fritz Strassmann on the splitting of uranium with neutrons were excitedly discussed. Says Seaborg, "I don't recall ever seeing Oppie so stimulated and so full of ideas. As it turned out, I was privileged to witness his first encounter with the phenomenon that was to play such an important role in shaping the future course of his life."

A visiting physicist who was working at the radiation laboratory in Berkeley, recalls that on the very day he received the news of fission, Oppenheimer started making rough calculations on the critical mass necessary to bring about an explosion.

The first experimental task facing scientists in the early days of 1939 was to confirm the discovery of fission. This came rapidly in the United States as elsewhere. The issue of the *Physical Review* that carried Bohr's article also contained reports of corroborating experiments at the University of California, Johns Hopkins, and the Carnegie Institution of Washington. The next issue related additional experiments; all had demonstrated the validity of the results obtained abroad. Before the end of 1939 nearly a hundred papers were published on the subject.

Although still engrossed in experimental and theoretical work on fission, the refugee scientists, Leo Szilard in particular, became concerned with what might happen if Hitler realized that through this new discovery it might be possible to develop a weapon with destructive power greater than anything yet known

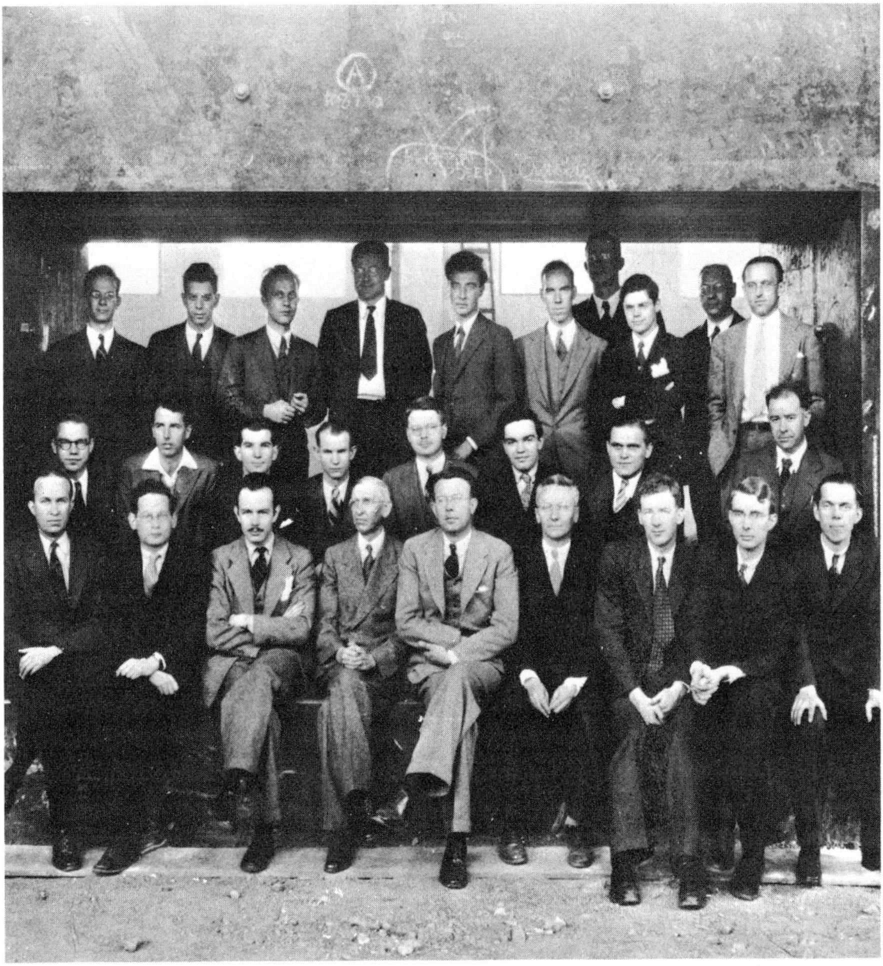

The scientific staff of the University of California Radiation Laboratory in 1938
UNIVERSITY OF CALIFORNIA

to man. A branch of government had already been approached, but little came of the proposal to push uranium research. Discouraged, Szilard talked over the situation with another Hungarian refugee, Eugene Wigner, and together, with outside advice, they decided upon a course of action. Szilard drafted a letter, which he persuaded Albert Einstein to sign. The letter was delivered to President Roosevelt on August 2, 1939. In essence, the letter asked for financial support to further explore nuclear fission. It pointed out that many scientists were being held in Nazi Germany and it warned that it was frightening to think what the potential enemy might do with the new discovery.

The President responded by appointing an advisory committee on uranium. The committee met for the first time on October 21, 1939. Joining the committee were five American physicists, three of whom were of Hungarian origin—Szilard, Wigner, and Teller. Einstein was invited but did not accept.

Most of the committee members were openly skeptical, and an army colonel used the occasion to give a discourse on the nature of war. It usually took two wars, he said, to develop a new weapon. Morale, not new arms, brought victory. The colonel's words prompted one of the physicists, who had been fidgeting in his chair, to retort, "If arms are so unimportant, perhaps the Army's budget ought to be cut by thirty percent."

The colonel's face reddened, "All right," he snapped. "You'll get your money."

It took almost four months before the scientists received word that the Army and Navy had transferred funds "to purchase materials for carrying out a crucial experiment on a satisfactory scale." The sum transferred was six thousand dollars—a ridiculous sum considering that two billion dollars would be spent during the war.

Scientists knew the alloted funds weren't nearly enough. They requested additional consideration. But the usual government red tape, Roosevelt's preoccupation with the international crisis, and the disinterest of the men around the President, all delayed action. But the men of science moved on to find the key to chain reaction. They realized that they needed a light uranium atom, U–235, that would fission and explode more easily than the heavier uranium atom, uranium–238 (U–238).

John Dunning of Columbia University persuaded Alfred O. C. Nier of the University of Minnesota to prepare small samples of partially separated U–235. Dunning and his associates then made the necessary measurements. In the March 15 and April 15, 1940 issues of *Physical Review* they presented their confirmation of what many others had suspected: if uranium-235 could be concentrated, there seemed no question that a slow-neutron chain reaction was possible. Although this meant power, a bomb seemed doubtful. If slow neutrons were used, the metal would tend to blow itself apart before the reaction had gone far enough. After deliberation, it was decided that U–235 might be susceptible to fission by fast as well as slow neutrons. Still, they had no proof. Thus began an intensive study of isotope separation—the separating of U–235 from the rest of the uranium.

By this time interest in uranium spread. Additional money was needed if further investigations were to continue. More appeals—more time passed—and more scientific interest was in evidence.

Then in 1941 the picture brightened. Vannevar Bush decided things were moving too slowly. He persuaded President Roosevelt to establish an Office of Scientific Research and Development with himself as head, and to name James B. Conant his deputy. Once appointed, Bush began pumping life into the uranium project; he also introduced the first security measures. No further papers on uranium research would be published in the United States.

Late in the summer of 1941, British scientists, the MAUD Committee issued their conclusion: the bomb *was* possible. Unlike the Americans, the British had united their efforts and did not have work duplicated in a dozen or more locations. When the British reached this conclusion they also had a good idea of size and method of assembly which the United States lacked. But as 1941 drew to a close, the progress of two years seemed negligible; no chain reaction had come about; no significant amount of U–235 had been separated; and only a small amount of the new plutonium had been separated. A bomb seemed remote.

Then, on December 7, 1941, Japan struck Pearl Harbor. The United States was at war. And with war came action.

"How soon can we have a bomb?" Washington asked.

Science and government would now play a new and intimate role. Overnight everything had changed. Science would never be the same. The United States would never be the same. The world would never be the same.

Although deeply immersed in teaching, Robert was still preoccupied with thoughts on the critical mass needed to start a chain reaction, and the work going on at the Lawrence Radiation Laboratory at Berkeley.

Frank Oppenheimer, by this time, had graduated from Johns Hopkins University where he, too, had decided upon a career in physics. He then went abroad and studied at Cambridge and at Florence. He married in 1937 and in 1939 received his doctorate from the California Institute of Technology in Pasadena. Robert was present for the occasion.

While in Pasadena that summer of 1939, Robert attended a party where he met a small, pretty brunette named Katherine Harrison. Thirty-five year old Robert's bachelor days were numbered, for as the story goes, Robert and Kitty fell "tumultuously and uncheckably in love." Kitty, who was married to a radiologist, Richard Stewart Harrison, attended U.C.L.A. as a graduate student in plant physiology. Kitty and Robert's intended marriage "rocked and bitterly divided two campuses."

Katherine Puening had been born and reared in Germany. She came from a conservative and well-to-do family. In 1933, while attending the University of Wisconsin as an undergraduate, Kitty visited a friend in Pittsburgh, Pennsylvania, during the Christmas holidays. During this visit, Kitty met and fell in love with Joe Dallet, a Communist.

Kitty married him in Youngstown, Ohio, where they lived in relative poverty. At his insistence, she joined the Communist Party and for a time worked in the Party office. But as time went on, Kitty grew more and more disenchanted with the Party, while her husband became more devoted. They separated in June of 1936, and she joined her parents in England.

Kitty returned to the United States in 1937 and enrolled at the University of Pennsylvania.

Majoring in biology, Kitty neared the end of her undergraduate studies. But before graduation she married an English physician, Richard Stewart Harrison. Harrison had practiced medicine in England, but before he was permitted to practice in the United States, he had to take examinations, and serve another internship and residency. After being married only a short time, Harrison left for California and Kitty stayed on in Philadelphia until she graduated in June of 1939.

On November 1, 1940, Katherine Puening was divorced from Richard Stewart Harrison, and a short time later she and J Robert Oppenheimer were married. It seems likely that Kitty may have found a degree of happiness, for her marriage to Robert lasted twenty-seven years. And these were not always easy years.

The year 1939 had seen many changes in the world; it had also brought many changes into Robert Oppenheimer's life. But by 1941, the only definite changes in his life were a wife, a new home, and an expected child. He had yet to see his role in the diverse scientific and world developments that had started in 1939.

12 ֎ PRELUDE TO ADVENTURE

AFTER ROBERT AND KITTY MARRIED THEY MOVED INTO A HOUSE
on Kenilworth Court, north of the campus in Berkeley. The Oppenheimers had decided to stay in California because everything
Robert dreamed of, in the way of physics, was developing there.
By 1940 the United States was no longer a suburb of the scientific community, and the universities in California had become
centers in their own right.

During the early months of their marriage Robert continued his activity in teaching and his investigations into fission.
Kitty worked in her field—plant mycology. Friends remember
that after Robert's marriage he blossomed as a host and that he
and Kitty delighted in experimenting in the kitchen. Another
friend recalls, "Oppie always made martinis with laboratory precision, but after his marriage, for some strange reason, even they
(the martinis) seemed to get better.

Then another change occurred in Robert. His reading interests altered. A colleague remembers meeting Robert coming out of the library. "Seeing Oppenheimer in or around the library wasn't unusual, nor was it out of the ordinary to see him with his arms laden with books. But this particular evening finding him with a dozen books on child care, child psychology, infant care, and so on, just struck me funny, although it really shouldn't have. I remember that I was still chuckling when I got home."

Peter Oppenheimer was born during Robert's session at Cal Tech in the late spring of 1941. A friend visited the Oppenheimers shortly after Peter's birth. "Robert was just beaming," she recalled, "and just like every new father, he jumped with alarm the instant Peter cried."

Story has it that Robert gave Peter his bottles, but never mastered the art of diapering. At getting a diaper on a wriggling baby, Robert proved as inept as he was in a laboratory. Even so, he delighted in his son. Some years later Robert is reported to have arrived at his own philosophy about rearing children. "Just pour in the love and it will come out."

Now that the Oppenheimers were three, Robert decided they should have a home of their own. Of this event in his life Robert said, "In August 1941, I bought Eagle Hill at Berkeley for my wife—the first home we had of our own. We settled down to live in it with our new baby. We had a good many friends, but little leisure. My wife was working in biology at the university. Many of the men I had known went off to work on radar and other aspects of military research. I was not without envy of them; but it was not until my first connection with the rudimentary atomic-energy enterprise that I began to see any way in which I could be of direct use."

In the autumn of 1941 a special committee was set up by the National Academy of Sciences under the chairmanship of Nobel Prize winner Arthur Compton to review the prospects of the different uses of atomic energy for military purposes. Compton invited Oppenheimer to attend the meeting; this invitation marked Robert's first official connection with the atomic energy program.

"After the meeting," said Robert, "I spent some time in preliminary calculations about the construction and performance of atomic bombs." Although burdened with a heavy teaching load, seminars, plus his participation in the management of the physics department (selection of courses, awarding of fellowships, and general affairs pertaining to the graduate council of which he was a member for a number of years), Robert and a small group at Berkeley plunged into calculations in an attempt to work out the critical mass.

In the spring of 1942 Compton again called Oppenheimer to Chicago to discuss the state of work on the bomb itself. During this meeting Compton asked Robert to take the responsibility for the scattered experimental projects. Said Oppenheimer, "Although I had no administrative experience and was not an experimental physicist, I felt sufficiently informed and challenged by the problem to be glad to accept."

After his conference with Compton, Robert called together a theoretical study group to meet in Berkeley, in which Professors Bethe, Konopinski, Serber, Teller, Van Vleck, and Oppenheimer participated. The group met secretly in Robert's office.

Compton again expressed his great satisfaction with Robert's progress. "Under Oppenheimer," he said, "something really got done, and done at astonishing speed."

But then, later in the summer, Robert got word from Compton that there was a question of his clearance on the ground that he had belonged to leftwing groups. However, Compton indicated that this derogatory information would not prove a barrier to Robert's further work on the program.

After reviewing the experimental work being done across the United States, Robert concluded that the efforts of all laboratories would have to be concentrated at one particular spot;

otherwise work would be duplicated and confusion would result.

On October 8, 1942, Robert met the newly appointed Chief of the Manhattan Engineer District, General Leslie R. Groves, and presented him with the single laboratory idea. Groves supported Oppenheimer's thinking, and a short time later Robert received a message from Groves asking that Robert join him to discuss further the idea of a bomb laboratory. In the limited space of a Pullman compartment on a New York to Chicago bound train, Groves, Colonels Nichols and Marshall, also of the Manhattan District, and Oppenheimer laid the first plans for the bomb laboratory.

Groves was considered the right man to head up the top secret atom bomb project for the Army. His new command was not officially announced until his appointment as brigadier general on September 23, but he had already taken up his duties. The General's most vital characteristics have been described as: confidence, intelligence, vigor, the ability to see through "humbug," and the ability to get a job well done. But Groves also had a less agreeable side. His high spirit, heavy humor, and sharp tongue often annoyed his fellow officers.

As one government official quipped, "In Groves, the Army already had a formidable weapon."

Groves's value lay in his ruthless single-mindedness. He had directed the building of the multi-million dollar Pentagon in record time and learned from experience how to deal effectively with stubborn contractors, careless designers, and self-serving politicians.

Groves accepted command of the Manhattan Project with reluctance. After three years in Washington, he coveted overseas duty. He knew little about the bomb project and the little he knew didn't impress him. But within a month he displayed his usual enthusiasm for the job.

Where was the bomb laboratory to be located? Inaccessibility was most important in selecting a site. Eight locations were suggested and six met with instant rejection. Then, one day in the middle of November, 1942, three men on horseback rode into the wilderness of New Mexico. They were Lieutenant Colonel W. H. Dudley of the Manhattan District, Edwin M. McMillan and J Robert Oppenheimer.

The three men studied the narrow valley known as Jemez Springs. McMillan objected to the site, while Dudley thought it perfect. McMillan pointed out that the location lacked enough space for a reasonable layout. Besides it was subject to flash floods.

Dr. McMillan recalls debating the point with Dudley, who for some reason considered the site ideal. Oppenheimer, with his usual concern for everyone's feelings, graciously tried to tell Dudley that he agreed with McMillan. "It's well isolated, and has a fine water supply," he said, "but the valley is hemmed in on three sides by cliffs. Don't you think that would have a depressing effect on the workers?"

When General Groves arrived later in the day, he took one look and agreed that the site wouldn't do. Oppenheimer then remembered a boys' school in Los Alamos and suggested they drive up and take a look at it.

Upon reaching Los Alamos the men found themselves below a gigantic, long-extinct volcano. Just to the west loomed the Jemez Mountains, the rim of the ancient crater. Branching out from the center of the crater lay dozens of deep canyons, cut in the soft red soil and through jagged pink rocks eroded by centuries of rain and melting snow. Lush green pines and shrubs spotted the yellow earth of the cliffs. Color was everywhere. From where the men stood on the 7,000-foot high mesa between two canyons, their eyes followed the land eastward as it sloped down to the muddy waters of the Rio Grande. Beyond, far in the distance, rose the majestic snow-covered peaks of the Sangre de Cristo Range. As Dr. McMillan recalls, "It was a sight to stir the imagination."

On November 25, 1942, the Assistant Secretary of War ordered the acquisition of Los Alamos. A few days later the first workers arrived on "the hill" to excavate the ground for the foundations of the "Technical Area" buildings.

With a site chosen only one problem remained: who was to serve as director of the laboratory? Compton suggested Oppenheimer as the natural choice. After all, he told Groves, hadn't Oppenheimer been the spiritual father of the proposed laboratory? And hadn't Oppenheimer proved himself to be an outstanding head of a team? Did he not know everything that was known of the project? Groves had been searching for the best man to take charge of the work. He felt that Oppenheimer was well qualified to handle the theoretical aspects of the work. But how well Oppenheimer would do on the experimentation, or how he would handle the administrative responsibilities, Groves had no idea. Oppenheimer had no administrative background. Says Groves, "I knew, of course, that he (Oppenheimer) had a brilliant background in theoretical physics, and that he was well respected in the academic world. I thought he could do the job . . . I was unable to find anyone else who was available who I felt would do as well."

Before the Oppenheimers left for Los Alamos, Robert and Kitty entertained the Chevaliers in their Berkeley home. Early in the evening Robert went into the pantry to mix some drinks. Haakon Chevalier followed. He said, "I saw George Eltenton recently," and went on to say that Eltenton had told him that he had a means of getting technical information to Soviet agents.

"This is a terrible thing to do," answered Oppenheimer.

Chevalier agreed and the two men dropped the subject but it would return to haunt Robert.

Robert was eager to begin work on the bomb project. He knew that he faced a difficult and challenging task with results unpredictable. Too, time was of the greatest importance. If the enemy developed the weapon first, they would use it without

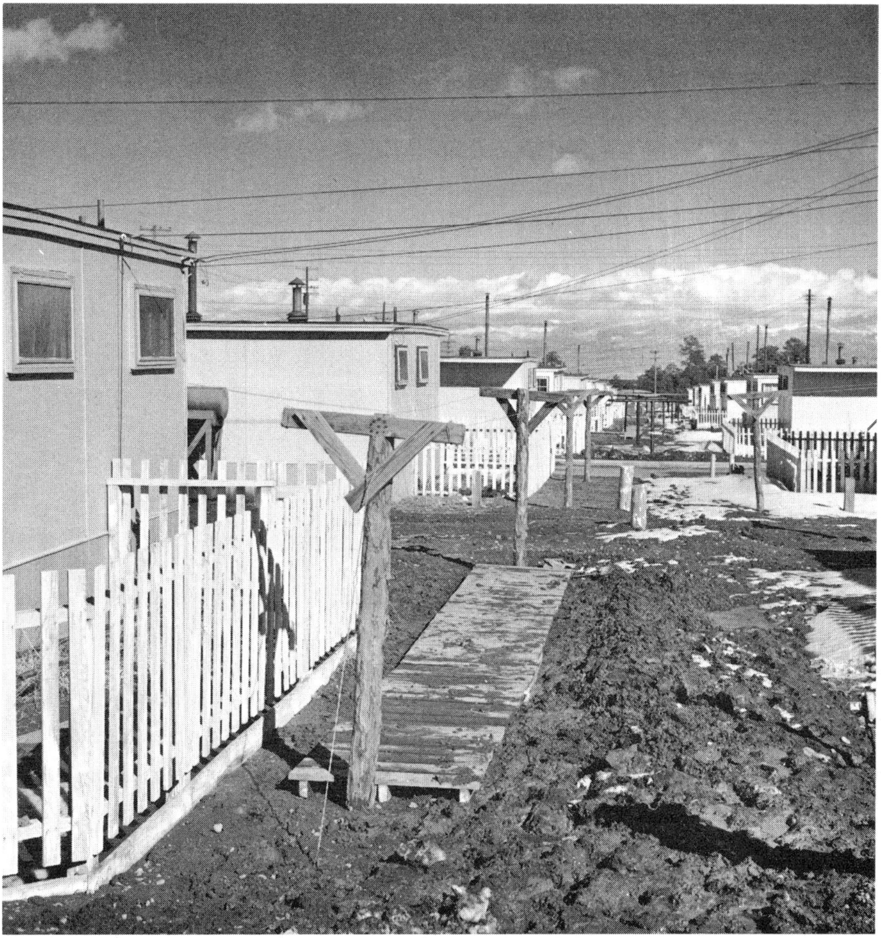

Housing at Los Alamos
LOS ALAMOS SCIENTIFIC LABORATORY

hesitation and without mercy. Many of the men who worked with Oppenheimer during the war years recall his saying, "if we could just gain a little more time, it would be worth almost anything."

But even beyond the urgency of the times, something else drew Robert Oppenheimer. The challenge of the unknown, the unexplored and unexplained order of the universe, the venturing of a guess on things which cannot be known, these are the elements of adventure—of high adventure—to the scientist. Robert Oppenheimer was a scientist. His mind was that of a scientist. For him, the days that lay ahead promised a height of adventure beyond his imagination. Other men would also be drawn into this work by fate and destiny rather than enthusiasm.

Although they were attracted by the "unique challenge of dealing with nuclear phenomena on a large scale, with taming an essentially cosmic process," a dark threat hung over them: what if they were successful? Often great new ventures and new discoveries are conceived and carried out only if men are bent on destroying one another in the name of some cause. If they were successful, would men see their achievement as only a new form of destruction?

III

IN THE
SHADOW OF
DESTRUCTION
(1942-1945)

13 ❦ THE "GADGET" LABORATORY IN SANDOVAL COUNTY

AFTER GENERAL GROVES HAD APPOINTED OPPENHEIMER HEAD of the new laboratory, he encountered opposition from military security. There was much in Oppenheimer's background not to their liking; past associations with Communists and leftwingers. Boris T. Pash, Chief of Staff of the G2 Division in California, prepared a report and forwarded it to Washington. Groves read it but found that he was already familiar with every item listed. Nothing new had been added. Writes Groves: "As always in security matters of such importance, I had read all the available original evidence; I did not depend upon the conclusions of the security officers."

Groves felt that Oppenheimer's potential value outweighed any security risk. He wanted the matter removed from further discussion, so he personally wrote and signed the following instructions to the District Engineer on July 20, 1943:

In accordance with my verbal direction of July 15, it is desired that clearance be issued for the employment of Julius* Robert Oppenheimer without delay, irrespective of information which you have concerning Mr. Oppenheimer. He is absolutely essential to the project.

While Groves handled security opposition, Oppenheimer threw himself into the bomb project. The laboratories and housing under construction at Los Alamos were hopelessly inadequate for future needs, and Oppenheimer knew it. But as he said, "It was a start." Construction, however, was not his primary problem. He had the responsibility of attracting and enlisting top scientific help. Oppenheimer's recruiting job was made more difficult by Groves wanting the laboratory to be a military post. The scientists objected. They insisted that the differences in rank would breed friction and bring about the collapse of morale. Besides, military organization would introduce rigidity, they argued. Most refused to go to Los Alamos under military conditions.

Oppenheimer presented the problem to Groves and to Conant who had become scientific advisor. They agreed that all laboratory experiments would be strictly civilian. Personnel, procurement, and so on, would fall under a contract between the War Department and the University of California. Los Alamos would have a military post; its function, however, would be subordinate to that of the laboratory. The commanding officer of the post would report directly to General Groves and would be responsible for maintaining suitable living conditions for the civilian personnel and for whatever security precautions the director of the laboratory deemed necessary.

Physicist I. I. Rabi agreed to go to Los Alamos, but only as a consultant. Robert Bacher also consented, but so strongly did he object to military regimentation that he said his resignation

---

* How Groves came to think of Robert Oppenheimer as "Julius Robert" is unknown. Some suggest that Groves presumed the "J" stood for "Julius."

would be effective the day the laboratory became a military installation.

Oppenheimer made going to Los Alamos sound more like an adventure than a wartime project. Top-flight scientists suddenly disappeared from universities, and from government and private laboratories. But perhaps Robert was too persuasive. People started arriving before housing on "the hill" was ready. An assortment of unusual tourists flocked into Santa Fe, New Mexico. They all headed for the office of Dorothy McKibbin, the Los Alamos Laboratory "one woman-American Express."

Mrs. McKibbin had ready answers for all inquiries and comments. She made lodging arrangements, located lost luggage and missing children, instructed all newcomers that their mailing address was P.O. Box 1663. After this she provided the "tourists" with names. Oppenheimer became Mr. Bradley, Enrico Fermi, Mr. Farmer, while others had names like Smith, Baker, Jones, and so on. "The Army wasn't very imaginative," said one scientist. "You'd think they would have thrown in at least a few American sounding names like Mashovilinsky or Gasoverez."

Dorothy McKibbin cautioned the newcomers that under no conditions were they to be addressed as "Doctor" or "Professor," nor were they to address one another in similar fashion. If they did, the citizens might become suspicious about the great number of university men disappearing into the wilderness.

After Oppenheimer had arranged for scientific personnel, he tackled his next problem—equipment. "We stole a cyclotron from Harvard, then stole two van de Graaff generators from Wisconsin," Oppenheimer wrote later, and a Cockcroft-Walton high-voltage accelerator from the University of Illinois soon appeared in the wilds of New Mexico.

While work inched along on the bomb, G2 kept a watchful eye on Oppenheimer. They still resented the fact that Groves had shrugged off their warnings.

In August 1943, G2's Colonel Pash had another session

with Oppenheimer. Pash, who had been investigating Communist activities at the Radiation Laboratory in Berkeley, had recommended that one of the physicists working there not be granted a renewal of his draft deferment because he was a suspected Communist. Oppenheimer had taken some steps to see that the physicist's draft deferment be granted. Pash called Oppenheimer to San Francisco to discuss the matter, and recorded the interview.

Oppenheimer, in what appears to be an attempt to show G2 that his eyes were open and that he was aware of the security measures needed for the success of the Los Alamos project, told Pash that he had been informed that technical information could be passed to the Soviet Consulate. And with this statement began a chain of events that covered ten years.

Colonel Pash was most interested in finding out the name of the man who had approached Oppenheimer with the idea of passing on information. Oppenheimer insisted that it was not a case of *passing on information* but rather it was *suggested* that it would be possible to do so. Pash persisted. Oppenheimer refused, choosing to protect Chevalier.

Still Pash persisted; he continued to bring the conversation back to the name of the contact. Oppenheimer refused to allow Pash to wheedle additional information out of him. Said Oppenheimer, "It is also my duty not to implicate these people, acquaintances, or colleagues of whose position I am absolutely certain—my duty is to protect them."

But Oppenheimer made two mistakes. He had not reported the Chevalier incident immediately after it happened. Only when he learned that secrets were leaking out of the laboratory did he volunteer information that he had been approached with the idea of passing on information. Then after he had volunteered the information, in order to keep G2 away from Chevalier, he told Pash that he knew of two or three incidents where an approach was made to obtain information. In his above statement Oppenheimer refers to "acquaintances or colleagues."

Then Robert made his third mistake. He grew impatient with Pash. More and more frequently he completed Pash's sentences. His answers grew shorter. He admitted that he was wrong in not coming forth with information earlier, but he would not elaborate. He said, "Well, I am sorry, I realize you would like more information but I am under a little bit of difficulty deciding what to do about it. The fact that I did not raise this question for a long time . . ."

Pash: "That's right."

Oppenheimer: "I have been in difficulty about what to do, realizing how serious it is. I think my general point of view is that there are some things which would bear watching."

To Oppenheimer the matter was closed. In so many words he had said that he understood the seriousness of attempts to obtain information; he admitted that he should have come forth earlier, but at the time he did not consider the attempt significant; and he assured Pash that he was now fully aware of what was necessary for the success of his mission.

But—Pash remained dissatisfied. He wanted the name of the man who had approached Oppenheimer.

Robert made his fourth mistake. His flair for the dramatic took over and he began to play verbally with Pash. At one point Oppenheimer melodramatically told Pash, "If everything weren't being done and if everything weren't proper, I think that I would be perfectly willing to be shot if I had done anything wrong."

Pash was not satisfied with Oppenheimer's declaration of loyalty. As he saw it, if Oppenheimer were truly loyal he'd have informed on his colleague.

Oppenheimer returned to Los Alamos. Pash, on September 2, sent a memorandum to General Groves insisting that the name of the contact be made known so that the investigation could continue. Then on September 12 Pash sent his findings and recommendations to his superior in Washington, Colonel John Lansdale, Jr., Security Chief for the entire atomic project.

Groves called Oppenheimer in and asked for the name of the individual who contacted him. Oppenheimer told Groves that he would not tell him unless ordered to do so. Groves allowed the matter to end there.

Landsdale, however, could not let the matter rest. Twice he contacted Oppenheimer. And twice he failed to get Oppenheimer to reveal the name of the contact, although he had used every trick known to security agents. But no matter what trick Lansdale used, the answer was always the same.

Lansdale: . . . "Do you now feel you can tell me who it is?"
Oppenheimer: "I do not now feel that I ought to tell you."

Finally the interview ended, again on the friendship note.

Lansdale: "I want you to know that I like you personally, and believe me it's so. I have no suspicions whatsoever, and I don't want you to feel that I have, and—"
Oppenheimer: "Well, I know where I stand on these things. At least I'm not worried about that. It is, however, as you have asked me, a question of some past loyalties. I would regard it as a low trick to involve someone where I would bet dollars to doughnuts he wasn't involved."
Lansdale: "O.K., Sir."

But Lansdale's "O.K., Sir" did not mean the matter was closed. On the contrary. Lansdale urged General Groves to bring greater pressure to bear on Oppenheimer to disclose the name desired.

In December Groves ordered Oppenheimer to reveal the name. Oppenheimer complied. Perhaps now he could concentrate on the job he had to get done. The matter was done with. At least it appeared to be. But appearances often deceive.

On December 2, 1942, Enrico Fermi produced the first

controlled chain-reaction and by June of 1943, Robert said, "we were finding out things that nobody knew before." By midsummer the laboratory organization neared completion. Hans Bethe headed the theoretical division; Robert Bacher, the experimental division; Joseph W. Kennedy led the chemistry division; and Cyril S. Smith handled metallurgy. Navy Captain William S. Parsons took charge of ordnance—the engineering burden; and the overall direction fell to J Robert Oppenheimer.

Many questions remained. Would a bomb work and what sort of thing would it be; how much material would it need; what kind of energies would it release; would it ignite the atmosphere in nuclear reactions and end the lives of all; could it be used to start fusion reactions?

During the early months there was uneasy cooperation between the United Kingdom, Canada, and the United States. But as time wore on relations improved and although they never became completely trouble free, Robert later commented, "From our friends in the United Kingdom, especially, we learned much and gained much from their help." A distinguished group of British scientists—Simon, Chadwick, Peierls, Oliphant, and others—contributed significantly to the project.

Delays of even standard catalogue equipment and shipments that failed to meet specifications frustrated the scientists. General inefficiency plagued them, especially the procuring of qualified personnel. Shipments, ordered by air freight, came in by rail; but these and other such annoyances did not hold back the work. Regardless of wartime difficulties and the isolation of Los Alamos Laboratory, the project moved forward. The laboratory operated under stringent security regulations which prevented contact between it and its suppliers. With all these factors against them, troubles were bound to occur.

Maintaining harmony and teamwork remained Robert's main concern. His charismatic personality played a significant role in his success. Says Victor Weisskopf, "It was most impressive to see Oppie handle that mixture of international scientific prima donnas, engineers, and army officers. He forged them into an enthusiastically productive crowd." Of course the project was not without its tensions and clashes between personalities, but as Weisskopf goes on to say, "He dealt with these problems with a light hand, and he knew how to exploit conflicts in a productive way."

One example of Oppenheimer's ability to lead and direct appears in the regular colloquia held by the men with white badges (the mark of a research scientist degree). Security opposed these meetings, wanting each man to know only his part of the work. Considerable dissension resulted. But Robert fought security officers and won. He knew that each scientist working on the project must know the entire operation if he was to be creative. Oppenheimer's battle with security on the issue of open meetings to discuss the problems of the bomb made them all feel he was behind them in their work. In truth he was.

Another time General Groves asked Oppenheimer if he would use his influence to persuade his colleagues in certain ways: Groves didn't want to increase the maternity ward facilities. To the General's suggestion Oppenheimer replied, "This seems hardly the responsibility of a scientific director." And as the bomb grew, so did the population at Los Alamos. Everyone appeared happy—except the General. Today many young adults have birth certificates stating place of birth: Sandoval County Rural, including a young lady named Toni (Katherine) Oppenheimer, born in 1945.

And as the population of Los Alamos burgeoned so did the project's ultimate object. In the secret gadget laboratory, in the activity of the best scientific minds, the embryo grew and prospered—a new dimension, a mighty change pressed toward birth in Sandoval County.

14 ⊕ THE PORK-PIE HAT

IN 1941 ARTHUR COMPTON HAD OUTLINED THE BOMB SCHEDULE:

> By July 1, 1942, determine whether a chain reaction is possible
> By January, 1943, achieve first chain reaction
> By January, 1944, extract the first element 94 from uranium
> By January, 1945, have a bomb

The schedule never changed. Almost overnight, physicists became experts in fields of physics previously unknown to them. Serious studies on the details of fission had to be understood. Oppenheimer directed these studies, both theoretical and experimental. Says Weisskopf: "His uncanny speed in grasping the main point of any subject was a decisive factor; he could acquaint himself with the essential details of every part of the work. He (Oppenheimer) did not direct from the head office. He was intellectually and even physically present at each decisive step. He was present in the laboratory or in the seminar rooms when a new effect was measured, when a new idea was conceived.

"It wasn't that he contributed so many ideas or suggestions; he did sometimes," Weisskopf goes on to say, "but his main influence came from something else. It was his continuous and intense presence which produced a sense of direct participation in all of us; it created that unique atmosphere and challenge that prevailed in the place throughout its time."

Oppenheimer's influence and presence extended to other areas. Even the workmen knew and loved him. He knew everyone by his first name. And as he strolled from building to building voices saying, "Good morning, Señor Oppie," rang through the morning air. "Everyone would have given his life for him," recalls Dorothy McKibbin.

Recently two memos were unearthed at Los Alamos. These memos reveal not only a little about the humble beginnings of Los Alamos, but also the devotion felt for J Robert Oppenheimer by the men working on the site.

The first is from Priscilla Duffield, Oppenheimer's secretary, to a Mr. B. E. Brazier:

October 18, 1943
At your convenience, will you arrange to have a table built for A–209, dimensions 26x30.
Mr. Oppenheimer would like a nail in his office to hang his hat on.
The middle lamp in the inside row, in A–210 has no string. One of the tubes in the lamp in A–210, which is nearest the door to A–209, does not light.

In reply to Miss Duffield's memo, Mr. Brazier sent the following memo to a Mr. J. G. Ryan:

October 18, 1943
Will you please build a table for Mr. Oppenheimer, A–209, 26" wide, 27" high, 30" long. Will you please build this a nice table, sand it and varnish it. Since it is for Mr. Oppenheimer's office I would like a nice table; he wants it for his telephone.
While you sent him a very nice coat and hat rack this

morning he would still like a nail for his hat. Please put one up in his office.

The location of the site fostered the closeness and effectiveness of the work. As Weisskopf says, "The location, which was Oppenheimer's own choice, gave it a special character by its romantic isolation, in the midst of Indian culture."

General Groves did not live at the site. He visited frequently. During one of his visits he took one look at Oppenheimer and said, "Get rid of that hat! Every spy within a mile of here can spot your comings and goings." Regretfully Robert discarded his Stetson and bought a smaller mud-colored hat, which he promptly shaped into a pork-pie. The pork-pie would grow into the Oppenheimer "trademark" in years to come.

In the fall of 1943 the Los Alamos *Daily Bulletin* announced that effective immediately all incoming and outgoing mail would be censored. Naturally this measure caused considerable consternation. Writes Bernice Brode, "We sent our mail unsealed, with the understanding that it would be read, sealed, and sent without a mark. If something inside did not meet with the censor's approval, it would be returned to the writer with a slip enclosed indicating what not to say. We were assured that the censors were faceless persons who lived off the site and knew none of us. But they were human, and funny things happened."

Once one of the physicists' wives sent a payment to an Eastern store with a note saying, "enclosed please find check." The letter was returned with a note from the censor, "Lady, you forgot to enclose the check."

During the second year at Los Alamos, MP's were brought in to guard the homes of the Oppenheimers and Parsonses. "Some of the practical housewives cooked up a scheme to use the MP's as baby sitters," writes Bernice Brode. "What could be safer than a man with a gun guarding the small fry?" Kitty Oppenheimer once got real service when her guard came to the house she was visiting to tell her that Peter was crying. But the sergeant in charge protested. His crack MP's had been especially chosen for duty on the government's top project, not as baby sitters!

Housing at Los Alamos resembled a low cost housing project. Except for the Oppenheimers, Captain Parsonses, and the post commander who occupied the three original log and stone houses remaining from the ranch school, the remaining scientists, army officers and their families lived in duplex or four-family apartments allotted according to family size. There were no paved roads, sidewalks, or garages in the town. Also there were no bathtubs, only cement tin-lined showers with dull black faucets, except in the few old ranch school houses where the Oppenheimers and Parsonses lived. The new residents promptly named these houses "Bathtub Row."

When the 7:30 whistle sounded each morning, Oppenheimer was already on his way to the Tech Area. In a short time the shrill sound became known as "Oppie's whistle," and many of the scientists awakened saying, "Oppie's calling."

Project Y, as the bomb project was called, moved steadily onward. What had started out to be an operation involving several hundred people required almost 4,000 by the spring of 1945. And as the project grew in number so did the curiosity of the New Mexicans. Amazing rumors circulated. At first people just wondered if the high guarded fence was to keep people out or to keep people in. But as the months passed into years, the stories grew taller. One woman who lived near the highway between Los Alamos and Santa Fe, wrote the newspaper almost daily complaining about the strange goings-on up on "the hill." She told how every day a great number of loaded trucks headed up the hill. Why, she asked, did they always return empty?

When a number of Navy personnel were attached to the project, some of the local citizens decided that a powerful new type of submarine was being built. To add a little spice to the story, some fun-loving chap circulated the story that the "secret

The pork-pie hat
LOS ALAMOS SCIENTIFIC LABORATORY

goings-on" were indeed related to submarines. They were developing windshield wipers for subs. When the men on "the hill" got wind of this story, they jokingly named the A-bomb project Mr. Bradley's "Project Windshield Wiper."

15 ❧ "THE RADIANCE OF A THOUSAND SUNS"

BACK IN MARCH OF 1944 OPPENHEIMER HAD TOLD THE LOS
Alamos scientific staff that there was no alternative to testing a
full-scale implosion weapon. Three problems faced them: de-
signing instruments to measure the blast and the possible effects
of a nuclear explosion; how to recover the valuable nuclear material in case of failure; and a location to test the bomb.

Locating a test site took top priority. When Oppenheimer
made his announcement to the staff in March of 1944, he had
also named Kenneth T. Bainbridge head of the test. Bainbridge,
a Harvard physics professor, proved an excellent choice. He
spent many months scouting across the United States looking for
a test site and eventually came back to New Mexico. One problem stood in his way. The area he had chosen happened to be
near the northwest corner of the Alamogordo Air Base. Bainbridge knew he'd have to get Air Force permission to use the
eighteen by twenty-four mile strip. He promptly flew to Colo-

rado Springs to see the commander-in-chief of the Second Air Force, General Uzal Ent, who gave his consent. Although he needed the approval of General Groves, Bainbridge knew he'd encounter no difficulty from the Chief of the Manhattan District. Bainbridge phoned Oppenheimer and told him the good news. He reminded Oppenheimer that the test still had no code name and urged the director to supply one. Oppenheimer had been reading one of his favorite poets, John Donne, when Bainbridge called. He glanced down at the words he had just read:

Batter my heart, three person'd God; for, you
As yet but knocke, breathe, shine, and seeke to mend . . .

"Trinity," Robert said.
"What?"
"Trinity," repeated Robert. "The code name is Trinity."

Despite the complicated steps taken to insure test success and prevent breaches of security, snafus occurred. Communication was needed between the ground and the B–29's participating in the test. The laboratory requested an exclusive wave length for each operation so that no one could monitor the communications. Months went by, and when finally Washington replied, it was learned that the short wave system for the ground was on the same wave length as a railroad freight yard in San Antonio, Texas; and that the ground-to-air system had the same frequency as the Voice of America.

Bainbridge reported later, "Anyone listening to the Voice of America from 6 A.M. on could hear our conversations with the planes." Naturally, a new request had to be forwarded to Washington, which meant more delays.

Urgency in securing manpower for research and development of the bomb continued to plague Oppenheimer. Men began working night and day, and Oppenheimer himself often worked twenty hours a day. His already lean frame shrank to 115 pounds.

Then a problem arose in the planned detonating system,

and almost all of Bainbridge's group had to divert their energies to it if there was to be a test at all.

Work began on the Trinity Base Camp. By December of 1944 a small detachment of a dozen or so MP's took up residence to guard the buildings and shelters while the remaining construction continued. As the new year opened, the implosion work showed more promise. With this promise the Research Division postponed even its highest priority experiments and turned to developing instruments for the test. By February the deadline was fast approaching.

Overall direction of the implosion program was assigned, in March, to a committee composed of Samuel Allison, Robert Bacher, George Kistiakowsky, Charles Lauritsen, Captain William Parsons, and Hartley Rowe. Because they had the task of riding herd on the implosion program, they were dubbed the "Cowpuncher Committee." The "Cowpunchers" had the responsibility for the intricate job of integrating the arrival of critical material from Hanford with the activities at Trinity in order to meet the deadline.

Under a cloak of secrecy, a maze of roads spread out across the desert and hundreds of miles of wires stretched over, on, and under the ground at the test site. By spring of 1945, a vast and complex laboratory covered several square miles of previously barren desert.

Frank Oppenheimer, who had been cleared for work in Berkeley and at Oak Ridge, had already arrived in Los Alamos and was serving as Bainbridge's troubleshooter.

By spring of 1945 urgent purchase requests increased so rapidly that it became necessary to inflate the urgency ratings used by the Procurement Office. Until that spring, four ratings— X, A, B, and C—had been used in order of decreasing importance. But by May, everything warranted an X priority and a "super urgent rating" went into effect: XX, X1, and X2. But

✿ *The "Trinity Test Tower" from which the first A-bomb was exploded*

LOS ALAMOS SCIENTIFIC LABORATORY

these new "super urgent ratings" didn't impress the manufacturers. They had grown quite accustomed to the desk pounding of the armed services and government representatives who demanded immediate delivery. Everyone had to wait six to fifteen weeks. The problem was further complicated by the security measures which prohibited any communications between the Project and the purchasing offices, and the stringent regulation which prohibited any discussion between Los Alamos buyers and the scientists. As one person affected by Oppenheimer's persuasive powers put it, "Had Oppie been allowed to talk to those people, we would have had the equipment we needed in *one* week's time."

Oppenheimer couldn't talk to "these people" but General Leslie R. Groves could. When he learned that the last available, nigh-impossible to get, instrument Oppenheimer needed had already been sold to the Nazi-sympathizing Argentine government, Groves did more than talk. He issued an overriding directive, and instead of going to Argentina, the instrument appeared at the Trinity site. With the appearance of the badly needed equipment, even the men who cared little for the General's blustering tactics softened considerably in their attitude toward him. As one scientist said, "The General knew how to get a job done and when he set out to do something, nothing stopped him."

Communications presented a considerable problem to the laboratory. Only five people were permitted to use the phone between Trinity and Los Alamos. To make matters worse, all calls were routed first to Denver, then to Albuquerque, and from there they went to San Antonio, New Mexico. Said one Los Alamos physicist, "By the time we got the message, we couldn't tell if someone at the site wanted a tube or a lube." The scientists finally decided the best means of communication was by hand-carried notes. They sent messages back and forth with the truck drivers.

On April 12, 1945, the American flag flew at half-mast at

both the laboratory and Trinity. President Franklin Delano Roosevelt had died. The decision to use the atom bomb would now be made by Harry S Truman, the new President.

As the test date neared, security precautions tightened. Anyone leaving Los Alamos had to follow the strictest of directions. They were permitted only to stop at certain places to eat and drink, or for gasoline. If stopped for any reason, they were forbidden to disclose that they were in any way connected with Los Alamos or even Santa Fe. If they had to give out information they were to state that they were employed by the Engineers in Albuquerque.

Yet despite the rigid security precautions, the lack of conveniences, and the delays and crises that frustrated everyone, morale remained high. Both the scientists and the military were inspired with a high sense of mission, duty and destiny. The overall picture was one of "cooperation under primitive conditions," even when everything and everyone was put to the severest tests.

Of the remarkable Los Alamos community Robert Oppenheimer later wrote, "I have never known a group more understanding and more devoted to a common purpose, more willing to lay aside personal convenience and prestige, more understanding of the role that they were playing. . . . Time and time again we had in the technical work almost paralyzing crises. Time and again the laboratory drew itself together and faced the new problems and got on with the work. We worked by night and day; and in the end the many jobs were done."

On May 7, 1945, Germany surrendered unconditionally, and on the same day the Los Alamos staff set off a 100-ton TNT blast as a "trial run" to check the equipment. The Big Three, now Truman, Churchill, and Stalin, made plans to meet at Potsdam for their final war conference. Secretary of War Henry L. Stimson advised Oppenheimer that it was vital that the atom bomb be ready for use on Japan; and also, that it be tested before the Potsdam Conference in mid-July. Groves and Oppenheimer bickered over the date for the final test. Oppenheimer argued that delays in delivery and development, as well as the tight schedule in production of active material, made it necessary to reconsider the date. No one at the laboratory felt the July target date could be met. But Groves was unrelenting. He insisted that the bomb must be tested before the Potsdam Conference.

Dorothy McKibbin felt the tightening tensions on the hill, but because of the security she had only intuition to go on. Something was going to happen; she knew it. "The voices on the telephone showed strain and tautness, and I sensed we were about to reach some sort of climax in the project," she recalls.

In the laboratories long meetings, attended by consultants, group and section leaders working on the Trinity Project, were held every Monday to consider the success or failure of the experiments, to correlate the work, to give progress reports, and to schedule the next steps.

As the Trinity date drew closer an air of depression and pessimism prevailed. A nagging uncertainty seized each of the scientists. This air of gloom was depicted in the parody circulated around the laboratory in July of 1945:

> From this crude lab that spawned a dud
> Their necks to Truman's axe uncurled
> Lo, the embattled savants stood
> And fired the flop heard round the world.

"If things weren't bad enough," recalls one scientist, "Hans Bethe told all of us, at a special meeting before the test, all that was known about the bomb, and all that wasn't. When Bethe got through, it seemed we didn't know anything."

On July 5, just five days after the plutonium had reached

Los Alamos, Oppenheimer wired Project Consultants Arthur H. Compton and Ernest O. Lawrence:

> Anytime after the 15th would be a good time for our fishing trip. Because we are not certain of the weather, we may be delayed several days. As we do not have enough sleeping bags to go around, we ask that you do not bring anyone with you.

There wasn't much sleeping being done at Trinity those last days. More than 250 men from Los Alamos were at the site doing last minute technical work. During the final week it was not uncommon for the men to work twenty-four hours, stopping for a catnap when they could.

The tenseness in the air grew suffocating. Not only did the scientists fear failure, they also feared success. Early in the project the challenge of cosmic mysteries gripped the scientists. But now, the thought of a nuclear fire kindled by man terrified them. More and more the men spoke of the ominous implications of their creation. Oppenheimer and Niels Bohr started many discussions about the dangers of atomic weapons. They pondered over how this devastating weapon could be turned into a constructive force for peace. Would it be possible to open the eyes of the world to the futility of war? Perhaps with international control this new force might be used to bring nations together rather than tear them apart. Many of the scientists half hoped the test would fail. But if it failed, it would fail before an impressive audience. Besides the many fine minds who had been working on the atom bomb project for twenty-eight months, General Groves, Vannevar Bush, James B. Conant, Ernest O. Lawrence, and England's Sir James Chadwick were all present for Trinity. William L. Laurence of *The New York Times* was the only newspaper man permitted by the Manhattan District to witness the first atom bomb test.

On the evening of July 11, 1945, Director Robert Oppenheimer left for Alamogordo and Trinity. Kitty is said to have given her husband a four-leaf clover for a good luck token. If the test was a success, Robert promised to let Kitty know by sending her a message: "You can change the sheets."

In 1945 Friday fell on the thirteenth. The scientists made feeble jokes about how they were about to foil superstition. But no one laughed much.

At the site, after months of activity, things relaxed, to a degree. The "hot run" countdown evidenced the less strained atmosphere:

> Sunday, 15 July, all day: look for rabbit's feet
> and four leaf clovers. . . .
> Monday, 16 July, 0400: BANG!

It was not to be that simple, however.

By Sunday evening the skies darkened; thunder rumbled in the surrounding mountains; and lightning crackled through the heavy clouds. Atop the 100-foot steel tower the assembled gadget rested in its specially made house. It had been hoisted up the day before, and except for the detonators the "gadget" was complete. Then the rain started—and continued.

Every five or ten minutes Groves or Oppenheimer would pop out of the dugout to check the weather. Said one observer, "The General seemed more worried about Oppie than the test." Groves himself wrote, "I was devoting myself during this period to shielding Oppenheimer from the excitement swirling about us so that he could consider the situation as calmly as possible, for the decisions to be taken had to be governed largely by his appraisal of the technical factors involved."

Would the shot have to be postponed? It was too soon to tell. Groves urged Oppenheimer to try to get some sleep, but for most sleep was impossible.

By 2:00 A.M. the weather seemed to improve; the test looked promising. The hour might have to be changed, but, yes, there would be a test. The waiting and checking continued.

At 4:00 A.M. the rain stopped. Minutes dragged by. Then at 4:45 the crucial weather report arrived: "Winds aloft very light, variable to 40,000 surface calm. Inversion about 17,000 feet. Humidity 80%. Conditions holding for next two hours. Sky now broken, becoming scattered." The wind directions and velocities looked good from a safety standpoint. The consultations began. One dissenting vote could call off the whole test. The decision was made. Trinity would go at 5:30 A.M.

Shortly before 5:00 Bainbridge, Kistiakowsky, and a small arming party made the final electrical connection, then drove away.

At 5:10 Groves left Oppenheimer at the nearest observation point, 10,000 yards south of the tower, to join Bush and Conant at the base camp, 17,000 yards from the tower at a point which would give the best observation.

With twenty minutes to go, Sam Allison took over the radio and made periodic time announcements: minus twenty minutes; minus fifteen minutes. Tension neared the breaking point. General Farrell who was with Oppenheimer looked over at the Director. Oppenheimer scarcely breathed. He clutched a post to steady himself.

"Aren't you nervous?" Rabi asked physicist Kenneth Greisen as they lay face down on the ground.

"Nope," answered Greisen.

Allison's voice: minus 45 seconds.

Joe McKibbin threw the switch that started the automatic timer. Now it was out of man's control. If anything went wrong only one man could stop it—maybe. The man eyed the reserve switch. He was ready to move if the order came.

Minus 10 seconds.

Cool-headed Greisen suddenly blurted out, "Now I'm scared, Rabi."

Zero hour. The world teetered on the brink of a new age.

"NOW!" Sam Allison cried, and as he did, a "New World" was born.

A brilliant, warm, yellow flash lighted the landscape. Al-

0.053 SEC.
N

100 METERS

The explosion
LOS ALAMOS SCIENTIFIC LABORATORY

most every observer felt the sensation of heat when the yellow glow flashed into a brilliant disk of white. Those who dared to look after the heat of the first flash struck their averted faces witnessed a sky blazing with fire. Then from the midst of the fire a huge red-orange ball, like an overgrown sun, rose, transforming into a narrower swirling column of color. The column spread out like a short-handled parasol surrounded by a luminous blue-violet halo several hundred feet thick.

"My God, it worked!" cried Greisen.

"I looked at Oppenheimer," another observer said. "His face relaxed before my eyes. I saw in his expression tremendous relief."

When the blue-violet vanished, leaving an outline of gray smoke splashed with the yellow of the morning sun, Robert Oppenheimer remembered another line from the *Bhagavad-Gita.* "I am become Death, the shatterer of worlds." The sinister cloud continued to rise over Ground Zero.

When the sound of the explosion reached the observers, it had a distinct quality of thunder, only louder. The original noise was a sharp shock wave, but because of the surrounding hills, the rumbling thunder struck one hill, bounced off, then repeated the action again and again. Five minutes later the hills still echoed with faint thunder.

During the greater part of the blast, Fermi, always the experimenter, had been busy dropping small bits of paper to estimate the force of the shock wave.

One of the military men had been so shaken by the spectacle that he exclaimed, "The long-hairs have let it get away from them!"

Robert sent his message to Kitty, "You can change the sheets."

The test was over, the project a success. The steel tower had disappeared, vaporized. And where the tower had stood there was now a huge sloping crater glazed with a layer of green highly radioactive fused sand. Tests would be made later; reports would be written. It would take two weeks to compile and interpret the Trinity measurements.

A short time later the men began returning to Los Alamos. Enrico Fermi, who never allowed anyone to drive him anywhere, asked a colleague if he'd drive. Laughing about cool, calm Fermi's reaction, a colleague commented, "The readings he got from his paper experiment were too much for him."

Oppenheimer had proved a successful head of the laboratory. Congratulations fell upon him. He had made all the important decisions and all had proven correct. No doubt he felt pleased and proud. But did he now have grave doubts and fears about the future? Many say he did.

16 ✆ A "LITTLE BOY" AND A "FAT MAN"

THE BIRTH OF THE "NEW WORLD" DID NOT GO UNNOTICED. THE light flashed in Albuquerque, Santa Fe, Silver City, Gallup, and El Paso. Windows rattled in Silver City and Gallup. So intense was the light that a blind girl riding in an automobile near Albuquerque asked, "What was that?" Telephone office switchboards routed hundreds of calls to local sheriff's and newspaper offices. No one offered an explanation.

A message was dispatched to President Truman at Potsdam:

TOP SECRET
URGENT
WAR 32887

Operated on this morning. Diagnosis not yet complete but results seem satisfactory and already exceed expectations. Local press release necessary as interest extends great distance. Dr. Groves pleased. He returns tomorrow. I will keep you posted. End.

The elated Secretary of War wired this message back to Washington:

TOP SECRET
FROM: Terminal
TO: War Department

To Secretary General Staff for Mr. George L. Harrison's Eyes Only. From Stimson. I send my warmest congratulations to the Doctor and his consultants.

Later in the afternoon Stimson called on Churchill also in Potsdam and laid the message before him. "It means," Stimson explained, "that the experiment in New Mexico came off. The bomb is a reality."

A second cable from George Harrison reached Stimson early the morning of July 18:

TOP SECRET
PRIORITY
WAR 33556

Doctor has just returned most enthusiastic and confident that the Little Boy is as husky as his big brother. The light in his eyes discernible from here to Highhold and I could have heard his screams from here to my farm.

Decoded the message meant: The second bomb would probably be every bit as powerful as the Trinity gadget. Trinity's flash had been visible for 250 miles, or the distance between Washington and Stimson's "Highhold" estate on Long Island. The blast had been heard for fifty miles, the distance from Washington to Harrison's farm in Upperville, Virginia.

By July 17 Churchill and Truman both knew about the successful atom bomb test. What should they tell the Russians? Even before the bomb had been tested the Interim Committee had recommended that the Russians be told of the new weapon. Russia was an ally. It took Truman eight days before he finally told Stalin. On July 24, 1945, Truman walked up to Stalin and casually mentioned that the United States had a new weapon of unusual destructive force. The Russian Premier showed no special interest. All he said was that he was glad to hear it and hoped the United States would make good use of it against the Japanese.

Neither Truman nor Churchill knew at that moment that the Russians already had complete details of the atomic test. Klaus Fuchs had seen to that. Fuchs was later convicted for his treachery.

The day after the Trinity test Arthur H. Compton forwarded a petition through channels to Washington. During the first two weeks in July, Leo Szilard, a prime mover in the original push to get the United States government to commence building a nuclear weapon, had circulated a petition among his colleagues. Signed by sixty-nine men, the petition warned the President that if the United States set a precedent for using atomic weapons, it might have "to bear the responsibility of opening the door to an era of devastation on an unimaginable scale." The petition asked that the President forbid the use of atomic bombs unless the Japanese refused to surrender after the terms were made public. In that event, the petition urged the President to make the decision in the light of the moral responsibilities involved.

But Compton had no sooner forwarded the petition when counter-petitions appeared. Discouraged, Compton asked for a poll of the Chicago laboratory. Fifteen per cent of the 150 who took part in the poll favored using atomic weapons in whatever manner would be most effective in bringing prompt Japanese surrender at the minimum cost to American armed forces. Forty-six per cent held for a military demonstration in Japan followed by a renewed demand for surrender before full use of the weapons. Twenty-six per cent advocated an experimental demonstration in the United States before Japanese representatives. Eleven per cent preferred a public demonstration and nothing more, while two per cent believed that the United States should forego combat use and keep the entire development as secret as possible. At the request of Washington, Compton forwarded the results of the poll on July 24.

During those last frantic weeks at Los Alamos before the Trinity test, daily decisions concerning America's future, the war with Japan, and postwar plans were routine in Washington.

In the spring of 1945 President Truman, on Secretary Stimson's recommendation, had appointed nine civilians to the Interim Committee. The committee's purpose was to draft essential postwar legislation on atomic energy, to prepare news releases on atomic developments for the White House, and to advise the President on steps necessary to prepare for America's handling of atomic energy.

The nine-man Interim Committee named a four-man board: J Robert Oppenheimer, Enrico Fermi, Arthur H. Compton, and Ernest O. Lawrence, to recommend postwar organization of atomic energy, which they called the Scientific Panel.

The Panel met for the first time on May 31, 1945. At this meeting they recommended the organization of an atomic energy commission. What had begun as a panel to recommend postwar action suddenly turned into a board faced with the question of tactical use of atomic energy. Should the bomb be used in combat?

Since Germany's surrender on May 7, Stimson had given one problem his primary attention—the surrender of Japan. Certainly the bomb was one means of attaining this objective. The Secretary of War recognized that continued bombing of Japan was necessary as well as the naval blockade. Entry of Russia into the war, modification of the unconditional surrender formula, and invasion of Japan were all ways to bring about war's end. But were they enough? President Truman wanted a clear understanding of American objectives in Asia. The sooner the Japanese started thinking about surrender, the greater the chances of saving American lives.

Truman advisors warned that if the United States did not take action to end the conflict and American troops had to fight on Japanese soil, heavy casualties were bound to result. In this eventuality, the advisors warned, the American people would not tolerate any concessions. The only recourse then would be to fight to the bitter end. Many suggestions were discussed but no policy adopted. Then the Assistant Secretary of War asked, "Why not use the atomic bomb?" With the bomb America could win the war without invading Japan, without the loss of thousands of American lives. Truman received the suggestion with interest.

Before a decision was reached in Washington, the military began to make target selections. They had never doubted that the bomb would be used. Why else was it being developed? Had the United States poured nearly two billion dollars into a whim of the "prima donnas?" Surely the "longhairs" didn't think this money had been spent to see if a weapon could be produced.

And now the scientists questioned whether the bomb should be used at all. "Pure nonsense!" said the military.

On June 16 the Scientific Panel completed three reports which Oppenheimer forwarded to Washington. The first report recommended that the government spend about a billion dollars a year to support an active program ranging from fundamental studies, to military, industrial, scientific, and medical applicaions of atomic energy.

The second report stated that the Panel believed the Manhattan District should be given the authority to undertake work of postwar necessity.

The third, and final, report dealt with the question whether the atomic bomb should be used as a weapon. The four scientists agreed that saving American lives was important and obligatory. They stated that the bomb should be used in a way to promote international harmony. Viewing the war, and not the bomb, as the fundamental problem the four-man Scientific Panel thought a military demonstration might be the best way to further the cause of peace. The Panel suggested that the United States approach its Allies—not only Britain but also Russia, France, and China—before employing the new weapon. In this way they hoped to enhance international harmony and develop a new frontier of international cooperation and world peace.

When the Scientific Panel's three documents reached the Interim Committee, the third report made a shocking impression. Of course, they would consult Great Britain; France and China were of little consequence. But Russia! Lengthy discussions ensued. At last the committee unanimously agreed to recommend to the President that the Russians be told of the weapon at the approaching Potsdam Conference.

Many problems rose at the Potsdam Conference. Stalin again showed his mastery at bargaining, along with his disinterest in the "new weapon of unusual destructive force." With the success of Trinity, the United States did not need Russian help to overcome Japan.

With the July 26 ultimatum to Japan unanswered, the course of action grew evident. Japan would have a military demonstration of the new weapon. The campaign to end the war would go as Stimson planned: first a warning, then a bomb. If the Japanese did not surrender after the first bomb, they would be warned again; a second nuclear blow would follow. This would continue until the government of Premier Suzuki surrendered.

President Truman sent the first warning. It was short and direct. If the Japanese did not surrender now, they could expect a rain of ruin like none ever seen on earth before. No response.

On August 6, 1945, a B–29 named *Enola Gay* flew over Hiroshima. The "Little Boy" whistled as it fell toward the city. The sight from the air looked much as it had on July 16 over Trinity. Fireball. Ruin. Mushroom cloud. Devastation. Mission accomplished. The deed was done.

"Fat Man"
LOS ALAMOS SCIENTIFIC LABORATORY

On August 8, two days after Hiroshima, Russia declared war on Japan. Japan still had made no announcement of surrender. The United States sent a second warning. No response. On August 9, 1945, the second atomic bomb, "Fat Man," hit Nagasaki. On the tenth Japan submitted a surrender offer. The United States presented its terms and Truman sent the draft to London, Chungking, and Moscow for approval. The answer was dispatched to the Japanese on the morning of August 11.

Although the military chieftains of Japan remained unwilling to yield, the Emperor met with his ministers of state and announced that his view was the same as five nights earlier. He considered the American offer acceptable. Japan must surrender. Emperor Hirohito instructed his ministers to prepare an imperial rescript to be broadcast to his nation. The Japanese Cabinet returned to its headquarters and formally subscribed to the terms of the Allies.

At seven o'clock on Tuesday evening, August 14, President Truman announced that he had received a message from the Japanese government. The Japanese had accepted the Potsdam Proclamation—unconditional surrender. The war had ended.

In Los Alamos bells bonged, sirens whined, and horns blared. Kistiakowsky set off a small arsenal of explosives in the canyon and everyone ran about hugging one another. Tensions built up for more than two years were released in an outpouring of cheers and tears. President Truman lauded the scientists. "What has been done," he said, "is the greatest achievement of organized science in history."

Before long there would be medals and certificates of merit for the men who built the A-bomb. To the public the name J Robert Oppenheimer would stand for the "father of the atom bomb." He was the man who had spared the United States from another winter of war. He had saved American lives. Oppenheimer argued that he *was not* the "father of the atom bomb;"

he was the director of the laboratory where the bomb had been developed, nothing more. For years to come, Oppenheimer would repudiate the over-simplification, "father of the atom bomb." But no one really listened.

On January 12, 1946, J Robert Oppenheimer received the "United States of America Medal for Merit" from President Truman. The citation read:

> To Dr. J. (sic) Robert Oppenheimer, for exceptionally meritorious conduct in the performance of outstanding service to the War Department, in brilliant accomplishments involving great responsibility and scientific distinction in connection with the development of the greatest military weapon of all time, the atomic bomb. As Director of the atomic bomb project laboratory in New Mexico, his initiative and resourcefulness and his unswerving devotion to duty have contributed immeasurably to the successful attainment of the objective. Dr. Oppenheimer's accomplishments reflect great credit upon himself and upon the military service.
> signed
> Harry S Truman
> President of the United States

How did he feel about the "brilliant accomplishment?" reporters asked. To one newsman Oppenheimer answered, "I'm a little scared of what we built." But, he added, "A scientist cannot hold back progress because he fears what the world will do with his discoveries."

Long before the decision to drop the bomb on Japan had been made, Oppenheimer sensed a change in the people at Los Alamos. "There was a great sense of uncertainty and anxiety about what should be done about it," Oppenheimer later wrote. "It" of course meant the bomb.

What did Oppenheimer mean by "uncertainty and anxiety?" The men who had worked so diligently to develop the new weapon had to ask themselves, "Is it necessary to use the bomb?" Secretary Stimson had to ask himself the same question.

So did the President of the United States. No responsible person could have avoided looking at the problem on the broad canvas of future implications.

On one side of the scale sat the unnumbered Americans and Japanese who would live to see peace if the bomb were used. Saved from more bloodshed, America could begin rehabilitating its war-ravaged friends and foes. Perhaps now, the world would find its way to world peace, a lasting peace.

But resting heavily on the other side of the scale, the future difficulties loomed. The United States could not maintain its monopoly on atomic weapons. American security rested on future control of nuclear arms. Too, if the United States dropped the first atomic weapon, how could America lead other nations in a struggle to remove this atomic threat from the world?

But this strange scale tipped one direction or another, depending on who viewed the arguments. No matter who touched it, or who looked at it, the scale never balanced.

The decision had been made and carried out. History recorded it. No one can possibly say what might have been if the decision had been reversed. Future historians may speculate, but there is no proof.

Shortly after the war ended, Oppenheimer received a congratulatory wire from the Japanese scientists on the "fine job" in achieving atomic fission.

Robert Oppenheimer had to make a decision. He made it quickly. He would return to university life. Along with teaching he would devote himself to international control of the new weapon. Many feel that because Oppenheimer had played so vital a role in the development of the atomic bomb he now felt responsible for its world shattering potentialities. Says a colleague, "Robert felt that he had to do whatever he could to see the weapon converted into an instrument of peace."

There are those who feel that Oppenheimer left Los Alamos because of the guilt he felt, for he had said, "The scientists have known sin." Oppenheimer knew and understood the frailty of mankind. In all probability he feared international control would prove only an illusion, a nebulous impossible goal. But he had to do whatever he could to make that goal attainable.

J Robert Oppenheimer would spend the rest of his life dedicated to this goal. He had committed himself, but he had yet to realize the extent of his commitment.

IV

THE

PUBLIC FIGURE

(1945-1967)

17 ⊗ "ONE WORLD OR NONE"

IN OCTOBER, 1945, J ROBERT OPPENHEIMER RESIGNED AS director of the Los Alamos Laboratory saying, "I'm not an armaments manufacturer." Many scientists had preceded Oppenheimer back to their universities and many were to take the same path.

One physicist at Los Alamos greatly resented the exodus of his colleagues, Oppenheimer's in particular. Edward Teller, a Hungarian-born refugee, had always been fascinated by "Super" —the hydrogen bomb. Teller had always believed that if atomic fission was possible, fission bombs could be made to trigger infinitely more powerful bombs—thermonuclear fusion bombs. When the Los Alamos Laboratory had been set up, the problem of "Super" was one of Oppenheimer's prime objectives. But as it turned out, a thermonuclear fusion bomb proved to be a bigger problem than anyone had realized and the project was abandoned for the more easily realized fission, or atomic bomb.

Teller believed that once the A-bomb had been successfully made, Oppenheimer and the other scientists would tackle "Super" with the same concentrated effort. According to an article in *Life* magazine, "He (Teller) was rudely disappointed when, instead, the whole top echelon began their great postwar trek back to the campuses. Teller stayed on at Los Alamos for a few more months, winding up his work. Then with a sense of frustration and of having been let down by his colleagues, especially Oppenheimer, he himself joined the exodus, accepting a professorship at the University of Chicago."

But Oppenheimer's return to the campus was not destined to be the quiet life he longed for. The postwar consultations began. Again and again he was asked by the President and the Congress for advice on atomic energy. Washington turned into a jungle in the fight for domestic control of the new weapon and atomic energy.

At the war's end the scientists' feelings were fairly well summed up by John H. Manley in his letter to General Groves of August 30, 1945. Manley told Groves that the scientists were deeply concerned about atomic controls and they resented being kept in the dark on the matter. Manley stated that there was too little contact between those who had done the work and those who were making American policy. The scientists had little enthusiasm for government work and each day more and more of them were leaving Los Alamos, accepting attractive offers from universities. Manley warned that unless the scientists soon received better treatment, the General could expect an even greater loss to the project.

Men like Bush and Conant saw the end of the war as a release from the bubble of secrecy they had lived in for four years.

And even before the war had ended the Interim Committee had suggested that a scientific office be set up under the United

Nations Organization. As the committee saw it, the United Nations could insure complete publication of all research in nuclear physics and would allow for free access of scientists to all laboratories where atomic research was being done.

At the opening of the University of Chicago's Institute of Nuclear Studies in September 1945, Sam Allison warned that Army security restrictions might force scientists to limit their studies to "butterfly wings."

The happenings in Washington during those last months of 1945 and the early months of 1946 could fill volumes and in many instances have. But generally it has been agreed that while the battle lines for control were forming, the Truman Administration tried to determine the best possible means for international control.

In the fall of 1945 the May-Johnson bill appeared. The unpopular bill provided for continued military control and imposed severe penalties for any infraction of the rules. The Army tried sweeping the bill through Congress. In October Oppenheimer had testified before the House Committee on Military Affairs in support of the bill. His testimony caused considerable irritation among his colleagues. But Robert had seen the bill as an interim means for bringing about quick organization of atomic energy. Within a short time he withdrew his initial support and backed the McMahon bill, which later became law.

Many debates warmed Washington in the fall of 1945. To add to the already near-boiling situation, the scientists were sparked into further action. They had gotten word that General MacArthur's forces, acting on orders from Washington, had confiscated cyclotrons from three Japanese universities and had dumped the valuable instruments into the Pacific.

The War Department, who now had as its secretary Robert P. Patterson, crisply replied to the scientists' protests by saying that while it was recognized that a cyclotron could be used for non-military purposes, the instrument was "of special value in atomic research which our Government believes should be prohibited to our enemies."

It was now obvious to all that the Army intended to maintain full control of atomic research, whatever its purpose.

During the war Oppenheimer had listened to Niels Bohr, who had clear ideas about what an atomic armaments race would mean to the world. Bohr believed that international control of the atom was the only way to avoid an arms race or, even worse, nuclear war. Bohr had not succeeded in his efforts to convince government officials, but progress in that direction did come about with the Acheson-Lilienthal Report in 1946. Robert Oppenheimer had played a leading part in the work of the Lilienthal Committee.

The Report called for the creation of an international authority to control all atomic energy work. The plan emphasized the need for a positive task for the international authority, to include the building of atomic reactors for peaceful purposes, and of atomic weapons, if necessary, as well as its functioning as a policing organization.

The American representative to the United Nations, Bernard Baruch, later presented the Report before the United Nations; Russia totally rejected it.

More and more the development of atomic energy grew into a mounting conflict between the free world and Russia. And more and more Robert Oppenheimer saw his dream of a "one world place" fade. The world thought differently.

Soon it became painfully obvious to Robert that with the birth of the New World, the atomic era, had come the death of his teaching career. His telephone, both at home and at his office, rang constantly. Usually someone from Washington was calling. He served on committee after committee. He acted as an advisor to many others. He lived on a plane. His schedule became so demanding that he'd often have to make four to six reservations at a time in order to get from one meeting to the next on time. Besides teaching and all the committee meetings, Oppenheimer had become something of a public figure. He wrote, "I had become widely regarded as a principal author or inventor of the atomic bomb, more widely, I well knew, than the facts warranted. In a modest way I had become a kind of public personage. I was deluged, as I have been ever since, with requests to lecture and to take part in numerous scientific activities and public affairs. Most of these I did not accept. Some, important to the promotion of science or learning, or of public policies that correspond to my convictions, I did accept: the Council of the National Academy of Science; the Committee on the Present Danger; the board of overseers of Harvard college, and a good number of others."

The Communist front organizations seized upon the opportunity to capitalize on Oppenheimer's public name. In 1946 while working on the international control of atomic energy, Robert received word that he had been elected vice chairman of an organization known as the Independent Citizens Committee of the Arts, Sciences, and Professions, Inc. When Robert read the organization's literature, he realized that their objectives were foreign to his own. He promptly wrote them and asked that his name be removed from their membership as he disagreed with their objectives. Later when the organization was cited as a Communist front by the House Committee on Un-American Activities he again wrote the organization and insisted upon resigning from the elected office he had never run for in the first place.

Oppenheimer's involvement in the political side of international control of atomic energy brought strong criticism from his colleagues. Many felt he had deserted them and their battle. They accused him of being a "scientific statesman" who moved in Washington's highest echelons, and who could no longer be bothered with hearing the voice of science.

Had Oppenheimer changed that radically? Those who knew Oppenheimer best and accepted him admit that he had a strong need for approval, almost an insatiable need. No doubt, to some degree, his need for approval, his deep yearning for friendship, for communication, and for companionship influenced many of his actions. Yet others found it difficult to believe that he had changed so quickly, so drastically, as to become the complete opposite of what he was, although he often appeared to have. These men claim that Robert Oppenheimer felt an intense sense of pressure about the control of atomic energy. Feeling this urgency, where was the logical place to begin the fight for international control? With the people? It would take too long to educate the layman on scientific matters that had taken years to develop. And even then, was not the public often apathetic? Hadn't Oppenheimer himself been one of the disinterested bystanders only a few years earlier? Also much of what he knew could not be disclosed to the general public; it remained classified and there was little if any hope of the information becoming declassified.

The decisions of a country are made by the men in power and the decisions governing atomic energy would be made by those same men. To Oppenheimer the place to start was with the governing body. He was in a position to be welcomed by that governing body, to be asked for his opinion. Also in the public mind he had come to represent all physicists. This could only be to his advantage.

Robert stood by his personal convictions and he did what he felt he had to do. For a man who longed for approval, his actions took considerable courage, for he must have known he was jeopardizing the very thing he wanted and needed most. He had once said there were times when he needed physics more than people. He was now fighting the cause of physics.

From 1947 to 1953 Robert Oppenheimer became a familiar figure in Washington. He served as chairman of the General

Advisory Committee to the AEC. He consulted with the Department of Defense on atomic weapons and on the general strategic policy of the United States.

Writes Hans Bethe, "He (Oppenheimer), and others with him, advocated more emphasis on atomic weapons for tactical use (so as to avoid a wholesale conflagration) and on conventional armaments. This earned him the hostility of some elements of the Air Force. . . ."

As the prospects for agreement with Russia grew less and less probable, Edward Teller returned to his work on the thermonuclear weapon. When he heard that Russia had set off an atom bomb and broken the United States monopoly, he believed that now a full-scale program would be launched to restore America's nuclear advantage. Then he learned that the Atomic Energy Commission's General Advisory Committee, of which Oppenheimer was chairman, had voted almost unanimously against any expansion of the thermonuclear work. It was a crushing blow to Teller.

The General Advisory Committee stated their reasons for rejection as technical, military, and moral. The committee also felt that the technical problems with "Super" could not be solved in the near future. Even if they were, "Super's" development would only increase the "imbalance" of America's military position, which would leave the country insufficiently prepared to fight small brush-fire wars.

The decision of the General Advisory Committee was, not long after, overruled by President Truman. But Oppenheimer's opposition was not to be forgotten.

As it turned out, Teller and his colleagues solved the technical problem the scientists had encountered earlier and a prototype of "Super" was born within a few months—just a few months before the Russians set off one of their own.

The General Advisory Committee had been wrong. Oppenheimer as chairman received most of the blame for the error, and there were some people who felt that he with his intelligence should have pursued the subject. But he and others as early as 1942 had given considerable thought to the project. The conclusion? "Super" was technically impossible. Teller's discovery had brought "Super" into existence.

In the early part of 1947 Robert Oppenheimer had been offered the directorship of the Institute for Advanced Study in Princeton, New Jersey. He did not accept immediately. He loved California and in many ways hated to leave the state. On the other hand the opportunity to be in a small center of scholarship appealed to him. Then in April, while listening to the radio, he heard a premature report that he had accepted the offer. As he said, "I decided that was a good idea. I have been there since."

18 ☙ SCIENTIFIC FIRE, POLITICAL SMOKE

THE INSTITUTE FOR ADVANCED STUDY, WHICH IS NOT A PART OF Princeton University, occupies about a square mile of farm and woodland. The Institute itself is just six red brick buildings and a new library. Unlike a university, the academic membership at the Institute numbers only a little over a hundred. It has no formal curriculum, no scheduled courses of instruction, and no commitment that all branches of learning be represented in its faculty and members. Unlike a research institute, its purposes are broader in that it supports many separate fields of study, maintains no laboratories, and above all, welcomes temporary members whose intellectual development and growth are one of its principal purposes. The Institute is devoted to learning: the continued education of an individual and the progress of the intellectual enterprise on which he is embarked.

Since its founding in 1930 the Institute has had but four directors; J Robert Oppenheimer was the third.

During Oppenheimer's first days at the Institute he had difficulty getting accustomed to the change of pace. He once quipped, "There are no telephones ringing, no committee meetings to go to, and no classes to meet. It's quite remarkable!"

Oppenheimer's new position as Director of the Institute for Advanced Study did not lessen his Washington activities. If anything, the Director became more deeply involved than ever. As Glenn Seaborg wrote in *Physics Today,* "During those early GAC (General Advisory Committee) days, Oppie also showed his great desire to foster the peaceful role of the atom." Seaborg goes on to say that Oppenheimer's contributions to postwar activities on peaceful uses of the atom were innumerable. Not only had "Oppenheimer spearheaded the move for strong AEC support of fundamental research," but he also "was a strong advocate of making fundamental scientific information available to all scientists and of distributing materials such as radio isotopes to scientists abroad, not only for medical investigation and therapy but for use in basic research."

There are many who feel Oppenheimer did too well when he served on the GAC and especially in his fight to permit the export of radioactive isotopes.

In 1947 Lewis Strauss, who served on the Board of Directors for the Institute for Advanced Study, and who had offered Oppenheimer the position as Director of the Institute, was also an AEC Commissioner. Strauss was considered the AEC's expert on security and was well acquainted with Oppenheimer's past leftwing associations before Oppenheimer was named to the Advisory Committee or as Director of the Institute. In August of 1947 Strauss, as well as the other members of the AEC, had voted to grant Oppenheimer full and final security clearance for the scientific post, chairman of the AEC's General Advisory Committee.

For several years there seemed to be no disagreements between Strauss and Oppenheimer, at least none were observed.

Then in 1949 Strauss charged, before the Joint Congressional Committee on Atomic Energy, that "American atomic secrets were being endangered by the export of certain isotopes to Norway."

After Strauss had made his charges, Oppenheimer was called before the Joint Committee to give his opinion, which he did brilliantly. After the meeting, Oppenheimer asked AEC Counsel Joseph Volpe, "How did I do?"

According to the Alsops' article in *Harper's,* October 1954, "Joseph Volpe recalls watching Strauss's face darken with fury during this (Oppenheimer's) testimony." And in answer to Oppenheimer's question, Volpe said, "Robert, you did too well for your own good."

The dispute over the export of isotopes appears to have ignited further disagreements between Oppenheimer and Strauss. These disputes expanded to include the hydrogen bomb; America's partnership with Great Britain and Canada in control and development of atomic energy; as well as a senator's charges of mismanagement of the AEC.

Robert Oppenheimer's life was woven into the times. The years from 1945 to 1954 in particular, are not easily explained. These were years in which science and government joined at a point of destruction—the atom bomb. These were years when the outcome of personal power struggles depended upon the histrionic excellence of the contestants. These were years when human emotions—envy, greed, hate, love, and loyalty—erupted with new intensity. These were years when machines called cyclotrons and reactors made headlines that sparked heated arguments. These were years when differences in personality and philosophy shook the foundations of nations—differences that could bring ruin to a man's career or reputation.

During these postwar years, against a background of malaise, suspicion, and frustration, a "Red hunt" sometimes compared to the "Salem witch hunt" began in the United States.

In England Klaus Fuchs, a Los Alamos physicist from the English Mission, had been convicted of passing atomic secrets to Russia. Ten top American Communists were convicted of conspiracy to overthrow the American government.

At this same time a cunning, over-zealous senator from Wisconsin named Joseph R. McCarthy decided the way to fame and power was to crack down on the Reds. He accused Roosevelt's and Truman's democratic administrations of "twenty years of treason" during which time they had "conspired" to deliver America to the Reds.

In the late forties and the early fifties, the House Committee on Un-American Activities made the news almost daily. The best description of this committee is probably President Truman's: "The most un-American thing in America in its day," he wrote in his *Memoirs*. Even today, the House Committee on Un-American Activities is frequently called "The Un-American House Committee."

The United States was nearly torn apart by the preposterous accusations of the House Committee and Senator McCarthy. Many historians recalling the period describe it as being one of the most terrifying in history. McCarthy had a country-wide following. Those who watched him on TV had little doubt that the Senator hoped to convict the President (Truman) of being soft on communism; even to succeed him. For success in dividing a country by sowing suspicion of treason in high places, history has seen few as effective as Joe McCarthy.

Between the House Committee on Un-American Activities and the "diabolical cunning" of Joseph McCarthy, thousands of patriotic Americans in government, universities, and corporations, whose only guilt had been in lending their names to some "front organization" during the thirties, found their reputations and careers ruined.

But while Oppenheimer waited for his turn at the stake, life moved on. Physics had been represented at the Institute since its

inception. But under Oppenheimer's direction the Institute became a center of physics. Wrote Abraham Pais in *Physics Today*,
"Once again Oppenheimer's talent for assembling the right
people and stimulating them to great effort was the decisive factor. . . . From the very start Oppenheimer brought to physics
at the Institute a new emphasis on youth."

When he first arrived from Berkeley, Oppenheimer brought
five research associates with him as the first temporary physics
members. Soon technical papers were published out of the Institute. He held seminars three afternoons a week. And as one of
his colleagues at the Institute said, "These young scholars were
by far the noisiest, most active, and most intellectually alive
group we've ever had around here."

19 ⊗ OLD INFORMATION BECOMES NEW EVIDENCE

WITH THE COMING OF THE EISENHOWER ADMINISTRATION IN Washington, Oppenheimer's official duties diminished. They would have lessened earlier, for while Truman was still President, Robert had attempted to resign from his position (as chairman of the General Advisory Committee to the AEC) when the President had overruled the GAC decision on the hydrogen bomb. Oppenheimer's resignation, however, had not been accepted.

In the early part of 1953 Robert's problems began to emerge and take shape. In June of that year the AEC had renewed Oppenheimer's contract as consultant for another year. Early in July Lewis Strauss became Gordon Dean's successor as chairman of the AEC. Within a week of Strauss's acceptance of the AEC chairmanship, he requested the Commission to take "initial steps to organize the removal of all classified documents" from Oppenheimer's safe in Princeton. Thus the first cloud of Oppenheimer's darkening future appeared in the political sky. But for some reason five months elapsed before the documents were removed.

In the summer of 1953 Oppenheimer and his family traveled to South America on a lecture tour. Shortly after his return arrangements were made for Kitty and Robert to fly to England where Robert had received the honor of delivering the B.B.C. Reith Lectures, and where he would also receive his sixth doctorate, *honoris causa,* at Oxford.

The Oppenheimers left in November. During their visit to Europe they hoped to stop in Paris to visit with Haakon Chevalier and his new wife, Carol. Chevalier's first wife, Barbara, had divorced him in California about the time he left his job at the University of California.

While Oppenheimer was in England, William L. Borden, who had been secretary of the Joint Congressional Committee on Atomic Energy, drew up a letter based on the information he had in Oppenheimer's file and sent the letter to J. Edgar Hoover, head of the FBI. The letter began:

Dear Mr. Hoover:
This letter concerns J Robert Oppenheimer.
As you know he has for some years enjoyed access to various critical activities of the National Security Council, the Department of State, the Department of Defense, the Army, the Navy, and Air Force, the Research and Development Board, the Atomic Energy Commission, the Central Intelligence Agency, the National Security Reserve Board, and the National Science Foundation. . . . As chairman or as an official or unofficial member of more than 35 important Government committees, panels, study groups, and projects, he has oriented or dominated key policies involving every principal United States security department and agency except the FBI.
The purpose of this letter is to state my own exhaustively considered opinion, based upon years of study, of the available classified evidence, that more probably than not J Robert Oppenheimer is an agent of the Soviet Union. . . .

On receipt of Borden's letter the FBI Chief prepared a summary report on Oppenheimer and on November 30, 1953, distributed it, with copies of Borden's letter, to the interested agencies, including the office of the President.

Less than a week later, on December 3, 1953, Lewis Strauss, AEC chairman, Charles E. Wilson, Secretary of Defense, and Arthur S. Flemming, the Director of Defense Mobilization, are said to have conferred with President Eisenhower. After the conference the AEC announced that the President had ordered that a "blank wall be placed between Dr. J Robert Oppenheimer and any secret data."

The Oppenheimers returned home from England just in time to spend Christmas with their children. No sooner had Robert reached home than he received a call from Strauss asking that he come to Washington immediately. Robert asked if it could not wait until after Christmas. Strauss insisted that the matter could not wait.

On the afternoon of December 21, J Robert Oppenheimer entered the white building on Constitution Avenue and proceeded to Room 236, Strauss's office. Strauss was not alone. AEC General Manager K. D. Nichols stood beside Strauss.

Although Strauss's attitude toward Oppenheimer had been less than friendly for the past several years, Strauss is said to have had some difficulty breaking the news to Oppenheimer. He began with the recent death of Admiral Parsons who also had played an important role in Los Alamos.

Then Strauss blurted, "Your security clearance is about to be suspended." Nichols, who later wrote about the meeting, says that Oppenheimer grew ashen, then offered to resign as consultant to the AEC.

Strauss handed Oppenheimer a letter listing the charges against him. Robert glanced through the letter. It had a total of twenty-four points. Twenty-two dealt with his leftwing associations prior to World War II; the twenty-third dealt with Chevalier; and to his surprise the twenty-fourth spoke of his opposition to the hydrogen bomb. The letter concluded: "raising questions

as to your veracity, conduct, and your loyalty." Strauss gave
Oppenheimer a day to think about what he wanted to do.

Admiral Parsons' death had been tragic for two reasons.
First, he died a fairly young man. Second, his wife later told
some friends that the day before his death her husband had
come home greatly disturbed. According to a second person who
heard the story directly from Mrs. Parsons, the Admiral knew
something was going on. He said, "I have to put a stop to it. Ike
has to know what's *really* going on." William Parsons planned
on seeing President Eisenhower the next day.

In the morning Parsons awakened feeling ill. He remained
in bed through part of the morning, then his wife took him to a
doctor. Before noon Parsons died of a heart attack. He never
made his appointment with Eisenhower, and his widow never
learned what it was her husband had to tell the Chief Executive.

Oppenheimer returned to Princeton and studied the list of
charges against him. The next day he sent Strauss the following
letter:

> . . . I have thought most earnestly of the alternative sug-
> gested. Under the circumstances this course of action would
> mean that I accept and concur in the view that I am not fit to
> serve this government, that I have now served for some twelve
> years. This I cannot do. If I were thus unworthy I could
> hardly have served our country as I have tried or been the
> director of our Institute in Princeton or have spoken, as on
> more than one occasion I have found myself speaking, in the
> name of our science and our country. . . .
>   Faithfully yours,
>   Robert Oppenheimer

The following day, December 23, 1953, Oppenheimer received word that his clearance was suspended and formal
charges were made against him in a letter from General Nichols.
A short time later, two armed guards arrived at Princeton to
remove all the documents from his safe.

Few people, even at Princeton, knew of Oppenheimer's

troubles. It is not known how many of his friends heard of the AEC action before April 1954. But one friend remembers Oppenheimer standing at the window of his office immediately after the security officers had departed with the documents.

"He (Oppenheimer) stood staring out the window. He was so deep in thought that he never noticed me. I turned and walked out of the room, without a word. But I can still see him standing at that window, like a soldier at attention, after having been disgraced, his epaulets torn from his uniform, his sword broken before his eyes. I'll never be able to forget it."

Only three months later did the public hear of the government's action against Oppenheimer. In the meantime, Robert had composed a forty-three page letter. The letter, dated March 4, 1954, addressed to General Nichols, says, in part:

> . . . I would have no desire to retain an advisory position if my advice were not needed. I cannot ignore the question you have raised, nor accept the suggestion that I am unfit for public service.

Then Oppenheimer goes on to say:

> The items of so-called derogatory information set forth in your letter cannot be understood except in the context of my life and work.

The security hearing *In the Matter of J Robert Oppenheimer* officially opened in Washington, D.C., on April 12, 1954. A Board had been chosen: Dr. Gordon Gray, chairman; Dr. Ward Evans, member; and Mr. Thomas Morgan, member. Besides the Personnel Security Board, Roger Robb and C. A. Rolander, Jr., counsel for the Board, and Lloyd K. Garrison, Samuel J. Silverman and Allen B. Ecker, counsel for Oppenheimer, were also present in the drab room. Dr. and Mrs. Oppenheimer sat nervously near Garrison.

The Personnel Security Board and counsels for the Board,

who were really attorneys for the AEC, had gone over all the FBI secret files the week before. Oppenheimer's attorneys were never to be given this privilege.

Writes Robert Coughlan in the December 13, 1963, issue of *Life* magazine: "Long before the hearing itself started, almost from the week his clearance was revoked, Oppenheimer says, he had no 'real hope of other than the actual outcome: once a thing like that has been started, they can't *not* go through with it to the end; and they couldn't let me win.' "

One of the people Oppenheimer consulted was Joseph Volpe, who had earlier been general counsel for the AEC. Volpe knew Oppenheimer's file thoroughly as he too had reviewed it in 1947 when Oppenheimer's clearance came up for its first postwar confirmation. Volpe read the AEC charges which Oppenheimer brought him and recognized that "it was a thorough mining of the same material—now being assayed in a wholly new light." Volpe recalls: "They had raised all the old data as if they were brand new, and on top of that had included the H-bomb question in the possible area of disloyalty. I told Robert I couldn't take part in his legal defense because of my recent close association with the AEC, but I could advise him informally as a personal friend—and as a friend I didn't think he had a chance because they had thrown the book at him. They were out for a conviction. And everything that followed was consistent. . . ."

Getting Roger Robb as AEC counsel was the first time the Commission had gone outside its own organization for a lawyer to handle a security hearing. Robb was a well-known hard-hitting trial lawyer. From the very beginning of the hearing it became obvious that Robb had no intention of conducting a "hearing." He operated like the prosecutor he was.

Volpe advised Oppenheimer to call the thing off, to resign from his advisory post. Oppenheimer refused. He knew that the day might come when his past would be dragged before him, but he had to go on speaking out for what he believed in, knowing what the consequence might be.

Robert assumed that his life was completely open. He knew that his phone was being tapped, his mail opened, and that his every action was kept under surveillance. But when he learned that his conversation with Volpe had also been "bugged," he raged. The security people had gone so far as to infringe upon "privileged communication." Their argument to this was, "Volpe was not Oppenheimer's attorney, but a personal friend." Nevertheless, Robert found the act "oppressive."

The public was refused admittance to the hearing. The tangled web of Oppenheimer's past, and the vindictive, inquisitorial spirit of the times in which his life was now being interpreted, filled page after page of transcript.

Several books have been written on the Oppenheimer hearing, and at the time, magazines carried dozens of articles. Joseph and Stewart Alsop wrote a hard-hitting article in *Harper's* in which they accused the accusers. Scientists across the country sent protests and wrote articles of protest in the leading technical journals. The July and August issues of *Physics Today* carried lengthy articles, and the *Bulletin of the Atomic Scientists,* September 1954 issue, published two full pages under the title: *Scientists Express Confidence in Oppenheimer.* Scientists from Princeton, The Institute for Advanced Study, Los Alamos, Chicago, the University of Illinois, and others all over the United States came forth in a storm of protest.

Thirty-eight people testified, both for and against Oppenheimer; oral transcripts were presented in evidence; letters, personal discussions, and so on—all entered the transcript. A government publication (992 pages of transcript set in type small enough to discourage most readers) resulted.

The *Bulletin of the Atomic Scientists* issued an article urging all its readers to obtain copies of the transcript. Said the editors: "It is the story of the life and times of J Robert Oppenheimer, an intellectual giant who became entangled in the Washington mare's nest."

Oppenheimer was the first to testify, and was not always his own best witness. He offered precise, fluent, and often impatient testimony, which showed much of the wonder and disgust he felt. The AEC Counsel, Roger Robb, took advantage of Oppenheimer's predicament and, at times, badgered him unmercifully. He insulted Oppenheimer and twisted his words:

Oppenheimer: "I don't know what the beginning says."

Robb: "You are quite right, it says you don't know anything."

When Robb addressed Oppenheimer as "Doctor" the sneering tone leaps out of the transcript.

Other times Robb threatens. When asking Oppenheimer to recall some minute detail in a conversation which took place eleven years earlier, Robb says: "Doctor, for your information, I might say we have a record of your voice."

In a question to physicist Edward Teller, Robb shows condescension toward Oppenheimer:

Robb: "In your opinion, if Dr. Oppenheimer should go fishing for the rest of his life what would the effect be on the atomic energy and thermonuclear programs?"

Although Robb simply employed the usual tactics of prosecutors, any reader of the transcript wonders, again and again, why the Gray Board did not caution Robb that they were conducting a "hearing," to weigh the evidence, and not holding a criminal trial.

Oppenheimer's feeling of doom is evidenced in all of his testimony. His words lack the articulate, brilliant expression so peculiar to him. It is as though he refused to use his most powerful weapon—his rhetoric. No doubt, he saw the futility of avowing his innocence. Truly, Oppenheimer had been caught in the "Washington mare's nest."

The hearings lasted three weeks—agonizing weeks for Oppenheimer. When the hearing ended the Board retired to make its decision. On May 27, in a two to one vote, the Board recommended that Oppenheimer's clearance not be reinstated, although they had unanimously agreed that Oppenheimer was a "loyal citizen." Ward Evans cast the dissenting vote.

Of all the derogatory testimony against Oppenheimer, Edward Teller's is unique. The Hungarian-born physicist told how he felt that Oppenheimer had lacked enthusiasm for the H-bomb program and how others after talking with Oppenheimer had become disinterested. But perhaps the climax of Teller's testimony is his statement that he'd "feel safer if the security of the country were in other hands."

Teller paid the price for his testimony. For many years he has harvested the resentment of his colleagues. Often he has been spoken of with cold, angry contempt. According to many, Teller was greeted with caustic comments about his "brilliant" testimony at the Oppenheimer hearing. It is said that before Fermi died he begged Teller to mend the schism among the scientists. Right or wrong, Edward Teller emerged from the Oppenheimer hearing a frightened victim of, not the "mare's nest" but the condemnation of the scientific community.

Who was responsible for Oppenheimer's troubles? In the legend that has encrusted the Oppenheimer hearing, the finger of guilt points at many different people as "instigators." Officially, Borden did. But if one checks the dates, it is clear that Strauss ordered the removal of all classified materials from Oppenheimer's safe some months before Borden sent his letter to the FBI. Some suggest that Borden acted on Strauss's insistence, while others claim Borden acted on his own without outside provocation.

The Air Force is an equally popular nominee. Oppenheimer opposed the Air Force in its idea of the way atomic weapons should be used. To top this off, Oppenheimer strongly opposed the H-bomb and did so until President Truman over-ruled the AEC Advisory Committee of which Oppenheimer was chairman.

Many felt that after the President's decision, Oppenheimer should have come out strongly favoring the thermonuclear pro-gram. When he did not and refrained from making any commit-ment he again aroused Air Force wrath.

Lewis Strauss is one of the chief antagonists of the Oppen-heimer hearing, say others. He had a personal vendetta against Oppenheimer who had publicly cut him down more than once.

As to the issue of the hydrogen bomb, Vannevar Bush stated the issue with eloquence when he testified before the Gray Board. The AEC letter, Bush said, "is quite capable of being interpreted as placing a man on trial because he held opinions, and had the temerity to express them. . . ."

Few who read the transcript are likely to doubt that, had Oppenheimer supported "Super" in 1949, he would not have been on trial in 1954.

The Board reached its decision on Oppenheimer also be-cause of what they called "defects in character." This accusation is most difficult to pin down. Oppenheimer had lied to security officers about the Chevalier incident, telling them that three at-tempts had been made to get information when in truth only Chevalier had approached him in a general fashion, commenting on his meeting with a man both he and Oppenheimer knew. Oppenheimer admits that he was wrong in telling the "story." The remaining arguments pertaining to "character defects" are dangerous ones. It appears that Oppenheimer was chastised for not recalling word for word conversations which happened ten or more years in the past. As one scientist said, "If someone asked me who was at a party I attended fifteen years ago, and what did he say, I'll be damned if I'd know." And yet this was exactly what the Board expected of Oppenheimer.

The AEC accused Oppenheimer, in 1953, of "persistent and willful disregard for the obligations of the security system." And yet, the only evidence to substantiate this charge was the Chevalier incident of 1943. Obviously, Oppenheimer had become a "security risk" not because of anything he said or did, but simply because he refused to collaborate with security until he was ordered by General Groves to reveal Chevalier's name.

George Kennan said, "All people are somewhat of a security risk." The problem as Kennan sees it, is not to seek "total absence of danger but to balance peril against peril and to find the tolerable degree of each."

Historian Arthur M. Schlesinger, Jr., in *Atlantic Monthly* wrote: "Is absolute security possible short of an absolute state? Robert Oppenheimer was doubtless at moments a cocky, irritating, even arrogant man. But surely no arrogance of Oppenheimer equals the arrogance of those who, in the frightening words of the Gray Board, affirm that 'it has been demonstrated that the Government can search . . . the soul of an individual whose relationship to his government is in question.'

"The government which claims to do this would hardly seem a government for Americans."

At the recommendation of his attorney, Oppenheimer appealed the Board's decision to the AEC Commissioners. A friend recalls Robert saying, "I have so little sense of 'self' remaining."

Oppenheimer was numb and dazed. The appeal was filed before the AEC. More waiting. "Robert seemed calmer," a colleague recalls. "It was as though he was glad it was over. Regardless of the AEC's decision, there was nothing else they could do to him. They had done it all."

The inevitable condemnation came—four to one against

him. This time Dr. Henry D. Smyth cast the dissenting vote.

Over—done—finished; the matter was dead, and with it died a large part of Robert Oppenheimer. He disappeared from the public eye with a quote from Shakespeare:

> The sad account . . .
> Which I now pay as if not paid before. . . .

20 ❧ THESE "INTRICATE CASUAL PATHS"

WHEN THE PEOPLE AT THE INSTITUTE FOR ADVANCED STUDY first learned of Oppenheimer's hearing, the mood was one of depression. The chairman of the Board of Trustees announced that Oppenheimer would continue as director. But the members of the Institute knew that Oppenheimer's appointment was up in a few months, and reappointment required a formal vote of renewal. Also Lewis Strauss was president of the Board.

Robert Oppenheimer took the outcome of the security hearings quietly but he was a changed man. Says Hans Bethe, "Much of his previous spirit and liveliness had left him." He retreated from the public eye and from the mainstream of physics. A friend at the Institute recalls, "He (Oppenheimer) almost disappeared from his friends' lives, too." The men doing scientific work ruled by government security saw Oppenheimer the least. "That's easy to explain," said one physicist. "What could we talk about? Certainly not our work. Certainly not the hearing, and not even the 'old days' for they, too, brought pain." And yet another colleague said, "Robert didn't seek out any of us or invite us to his home. I think he feared an invitation might jeopardize our security clearances. We invited him out, or to our homes, but for quite a while he declined, graciously, of course, but he declined."

Even after the hearing Oppenheimer was watched, his phone tapped and his mail opened. To his cousin he said, "They are spending more to have my phone tapped than they paid me for my work at Los Alamos." And once when he was followed to the airport, he looked over his shoulder at the three security guards and said to a friend, "They're afraid I'll defect to Russia."

Recalls friend and colleague Harold Cherniss, "In a sense, he seemed relieved to have it done with." For years Robert had lived under the cloud and perhaps, as Cherniss said, "Although he was very much hurt and felt that he had been misused, he felt relieved that he no longer had to wonder when the storm would break." Then Cherniss adds, "But who knows how he felt inwardly?"

Former Ambassador to Russia, George Kennan, remembers drawing Oppenheimer's attention to the fact that he would be welcome in a hundred academic centers abroad. Says Kennan, "I asked him whether he had not thought of taking residence outside this country. His answer, given to me with tears in his eyes: 'Damn it, I happen to love this country.' "

Many people have said that after the hearing Oppenheimer was a different person. He looked frail, and he had an almost saintly quality about him; he became gentle, more tolerant, and showed a greater degree of compassion and worldly understanding. When one of Oppenheimer's old students visited Princeton several months after the hearing, he remembers "how Oppie had aged. He had always appeared younger than he was, but now at fifty, he looked much older." Other observers noticed that

Oppenheimer's hair had grayed and the light was gone from his eyes. "It was tragic," said a friend.

But Robert Oppenheimer was not a man who looked at life in the past tense. To his cousin he said, "I can't find it in my heart to hate my enemies."

The men at the Institute, as well as most of the scientific community, had backed Robert. The Board of Trustees of the Institute offered him reappointment as director, and he accepted. Strauss is reported as saying, "security" was not involved in this job. But as one Princeton University physicist said, "The AEC had found Oppenheimer 'loyal' but they also branded him a security risk. The public found this distinction too obscure to grasp. In the minds of many people, Oppenheimer stood convicted. In their eyes he was a subversive, or worse, a Communist. Oppenheimer had to live with this stigma."

"The family was hit hard," a friend recalls. "Peter, a very sensitive boy, was in high school then, and he suffered under his classmates. Toni was younger and didn't seem to get the brunt of it that her brother did."

At the Institute for Advanced Study Oppenheimer still took an active part in physics. He later said, "We have, all of us, to preserve our competence in our own professions, to preserve what we know intimately, to preserve our mastery. This is, in fact, our only anchor with honesty." During his darkest days it was a great comfort for Oppenheimer to see physics flourish at the Institute.

Excluded from government work and denied this release for his mental energies, Oppenheimer moved on to be the voice of science. He was as interested and well informed on physics as ever, still a leading figure at international conferences. His activities now moved along more general lines—the public understanding of science. His Reith Lectures were published in a book under the title *Science and the Common Understanding.*

This collection is among the most lucid and, at the same time, most profound expositions of atomic and quantum theory presented for the layman. But even in his writing Oppenheimer did not take the easy way. He did not present the facts alone, but chose to interpret humanistically the meaning of the revolution in scientific thinking. *Science and the Common Understanding,* wrote John Mason Brown, "is the work of a scientist who is an artist and an artist who is a poet."

In June of 1954 another book was running through the presses, and it was destined to create a sensation. The title: *In the Matter of J Robert Oppenheimer: Transcript of Hearing Before Personnel Security Board,* April 12, 1954 through May 6, 1954.

The following month, on the twenty-fifth, the *Washington Post* reviewed the book:

> The Government Printing Office a few weeks ago turned up as the unlikely publisher of the most significant and controversial book of the year.
>
> It is about the length of the Bible, has a plot more intricate than *Gone With the Wind* and half as many characters as *War and Peace.* Depending on your reading speed it takes from twenty to thirty solid hours to complete.
>
> It reflects on the troubled social and political world about us perhaps more deeply and disturbingly than any other book published during the cold war.
>
> It is a treasure trove for statesmen, moralists, scientists and military intelligence officers on both sides of the iron curtain. It is a source book for a generation of historians to come. It is quite probably the raw material for dozens of future dramatists, novelists and social philosophers. . . .

As John Mason Brown aptly put it, "reading it, rereading it, and living with its complexities, more than being a job, is almost a profession."

Not included in this monumental transcript of the hearing are the texts of principal documents and letters. They followed in a second publication, which also bore the same title. Of the two texts, AEC Commissioner Henry D. Smyth, who had cast the dissenting vote, offers perhaps the soundest advice: "I urge thoughtful citizens to examine this testimony for themselves, and not to be content with summaries or with extracts out of context."

Robert Oppenheimer wanted to forget as much of those weeks, those months, as was humanly possible. He had set his new course: common understanding. At first he addressed himself to the "intellectual community." He wanted to foster a common understanding within this community. Then, as an example of what he felt could be properly shared, he mentioned the lesson of quantum theory, known to the physicist as complementarity. "He wished, and in fact tried, to explain this lesson to the biologist, the statesman and the artist because he believed that what to a physicist is a technique, represents at the same time a general way of thinking that could be liberating to all," wrote Abraham Pais in *Physics Today*. Physicist Pais goes on to say that Oppenheimer "saw a twofold duty in the educational system." In the face of increasing demands on education men should "continue to stress that the cultural life of science lies almost entirely in the intimate view of the professional." Oppenheimer himself said, "No man should escape our universities without . . . some sense of the fact that not through his fault, but in the nature of things, he is going to be an ignorant man, and so is everyone else."

He devoted the remainder of his life to traveling, lecturing, writing, and, of course, the advancement of physics. But by the summer of 1955 Oppenheimer badly needed a rest. The burdens of the past ten years had demanded activity far in excess of his strength. He did what many men have done; he turned to the sea to find peace and nourishment for his exhausted body and spirit. He chartered the *Mollyhawk,* a seventy-foot schooner-rigged yacht, from Captain Dennis Nicholson, and the entire family boarded the vessel at Tobago, British West Indies, for a six week cruise.

After this trip the Oppenheimers returned to the Caribbean for a part of each summer and sometimes over Christmas vacation. Later they bought land on St. John's Island, and by 1960 a house was built at Hawk's Nest Bay. But Robert was not destined to spend much time on St. John's Island.

Back in the United States there were those who could not, or would not, allow the 1954 security hearing to die. When in 1961 the Organization of American States inaugurated its Professorship Program, it was decided that to give special impetus to the program a distinguished scholar should be engaged to offer instruction in a field in which a Latin American country lacked competent teachers. The OAS chose Dr. J Robert Oppenheimer who was not only a brilliant scholar but one of international stature.

While Latin America reacted with overwhelming enthusiasm when the OAS announced its choice, men on Capitol Hill protested. These men suggested that Dr. Oppenheimer's appointment was counter to United States interests, and they also raised doubts whether funds contributed by the American Government to an international organization should be used to send a citizen of "questionable standing" abroad.

But the witch-burning days were past and after a flurry of newspaper headlines, the matter died down and was forgotten. Even if it had gone on, however, the OAS would have persisted in its choice, for as the organization said, "visiting professors, like all others in OAS employ, are not considered as nationalists representing individual countries, but as international civil servants working on behalf of all our member states."

Certainly the OAS's stand took moral courage and showed devotion to principle, for opposition from Capitol Hill could have resulted in the loss of American financial aid.

Ralph Dimmick, OAS Special Assistant to the Secretary

General, writes, when "Dr. Oppenheimer called on the Secretary General before departing on the trip, all were impressed by his simplicity and modesty." Oppenheimer told the Secretary General that he was "deeply honored" when Dr. Mora handed him his OAS Official Travel Document.

Oppenheimer's Latin American tour began in June 1961:

Mexico—	Institute of Physics, University of Mexico, from June 4 to 13, 1961.
Argentina—	School of Exact Sciences of the University of Buenos Aires, from September 10 to 16, 1961.
Brazil—	Brazilian Physics Research Center in Rio de Janeiro, from September 16 to 25, 1961.

According to OAS reports, Oppenheimer's tour was a huge success, and the Director of the Institute for Advanced Study charmed and impressed everyone he met.

"The tragedy of 1954 ended Oppenheimer's direct connection with the government of the United States. In spite of it, his influence in this country and abroad was not lessened; perhaps it was enhanced," recalls Henry D. Smyth, Professor Emeritus of physics, Princeton University.

Evidence substantiates Dr. Smyth's words. Oppenheimer was invited to lecture, not only in the United States, but abroad as well: Germany, Switzerland, Canada, Belgium, Latin America, England, France, Denmark, and so on. His lectures were compiled into books and translated into French, German, Spanish, Japanese, Norwegian, Danish, Serbo-Croat, and even Russian. Governments gave him special honors; European societies of science opened memberships to him;* and universities in

* From 1941 Oppenheimer was a member of the National Academy of Sciences and also a fellow of the American Physical Society, the American Philosophical Society, the American Academy of Arts and Sciences and a member of the Brazilian, Danish, and Japanese Royal Academies of Science.

In 1958 the French Government awarded Oppenheimer the *Legion d' honneur*.

Europe presented him with honorary doctorates. He became an international figure in great demand.

J Robert Oppenheimer spent the last thirteen years of his life attempting to communicate with man. His rhetoric does not lend itself well to fragmentation. Although his works form a compact, related system, when the reader attempts to divide the material, a certain relationship is broken. Yet, when viewed as a whole, the reader clearly sees all the profound truths of the universe stated simply.

In speaking of the common threads of the arts and sciences, Oppenheimer says:

> Both the man of science and the man of art live always at the edge of mystery . . . they can, in their work and in their lives, help themselves, help one another, and help all men . . .

When he speaks of "community" Oppenheimer stresses the need for more learning:

> In a free world . . . we need to do more: we need to cherish man's curiosity, his understanding, his love, so that he may indeed learn what is new and hard and deep.

Throughout his lectures and writings, whether stated implicitly or explicitly, an emphasis on the need for *communication* remains paramount in his rhetoric:

> Someone will say "You seem to worry about communication. Isn't that all?" I think it is all. Civilization, all we are, all we know, all we can do, rests on our power to tell each other about things. We do that in more ways than words; but if we do not do that, we are not human. . . .

In 1954 Oppenheimer made a noble plea for *The Open Mind*. He said, because we are human:

> we shall have a rugged time of it to keep our minds open and to keep them deep, to keep our sense of beauty and our ability to make it, and our occasional ability to see it in places remote and strange and unfamiliar; we shall have a rugged time of it,

all of us, in keeping these gardens in our villages, in keeping open the manifold, intricate, casual paths, to keep these flourishing in a great, open, windy world; but this, as I see it, is the condition of man; and in this condition we can help, because we can love one another.

But by 1960 his plea grew more urgent, more intense. In an address before the Tenth Anniversary Conference Congress for Cultural freedom in Berlin, June 1960, he again touched on his frequent theme, "tradition." But the entire address centers around his paramount theme: communication, the need for common understanding:

> I have been much concerned that in this world we have so largely lost the ability to talk with one another. In the great succession of deep discoveries, we have had neither the time nor the skill nor the dedication to tell one another what we have learned, nor to listen, nor to hear, nor to welcome its enrichment of the common culture and the common understanding. Thus the public sector of our lives, what we have and hold in common, has suffered as have the illumination of the arts, the deepening of justice, and virtue, the ennobling of power and of our common discourse. We are less men for this. . . . We hunger for nobility: the rare words and acts that harmonize simplicity and truth. In this I see some connection with the great unsolved public problems: survival, liberty, fraternity. . . .

Oppenheimer then goes on to say that the intellectual community must put forth a much greater effort than in the past, and as the point of departure he suggests:

> . . . we must learn again, without contempt and with great patience, to talk to one another; and we must hear.

21 ❧ AN EVENING WALK AT NOON

IN HIS LIFETIME J ROBERT OPPENHEIMER RECEIVED THREE honors from three Presidents. Harry S Truman had awarded Oppenheimer the Medal for Merit for his work at Los Alamos. John F. Kennedy honored Oppenheimer in the way of an invitation to a White House dinner given in honor of Nobel Prize winners. Many feel that President Kennedy's act was a first step—an apology—for the wrongs committed against Oppenheimer in 1954.

On the morning of November 22, 1963, in Dallas, John F. Kennedy approved Oppenheimer for the Fermi Award, and announced that, despite the coming election year, he would personally make the presentation. That afternoon the President of the United States was assassinated.

Many believed that had Kennedy lived, he would have restored Oppenheimer's clearance and thus erased the official stigma which had been placed on the scientist. Many hoped that

President Johnson would pick up where Kennedy left off; unfortunately he did not.

The date December 2 marked the advent of a new age. It was on the second of December 1942 that Enrico Fermi achieved man's first controlled nuclear chain reaction and opened the door to the atomic age. Fermi died in 1956. In honor of his memory, the Atomic Energy Commission created the annual Enrico Fermi award: a gold medal, a citation, and a tax-free check for $50,000; and annually on December 2 the AEC presented this award to an individual who had advanced atomic science.

Six men since Fermi had won this award. J Robert Oppenheimer was to be the seventh.

Keeping his word to the dead Fermi, Edward Teller, 1962 Award Winner, had cast his vote in Oppenheimer's favor. Perhaps now the chasm opened between men of science would be bridged, and all could work together for the benefit of mankind. Teller hoped so, and certainly Oppenheimer shared his dream.

The December date was significant in another way. It was exactly ten years, plus one day, since a "blank wall" had been ordered between Oppenheimer and all classified documents. And this too happened at the White House.

On December 2, 1963, fifty-nine year old J Robert Oppenheimer walked through the doors of the White House Cabinet Room. He wore the same frail inquiring look known throughout the world but he was not the same, and everyone in the room knew it. Many who had not seen him for some time felt sick and guilty because of the change they saw in him. White haired, ghostly thin, always sensitive to the feelings of others, perhaps Oppenheimer felt it too, for his tension and emotion refused to remain hidden. At moments many thought—feared—he would lose his customary composure. He didn't.

Glenn Seaborg, AEC Chairman, opened the proceedings: "Mr. President, I have the honor to present Dr. J Robert

✿ *Presentation of the Enrico Fermi Award on December 2,*
1963
UNITED STATES ATOMIC ENERGY COMMISSION

Oppenheimer as the seventh recipient of the Enrico Fermi Award."

Seaborg then read the citation:

FOR CONTRIBUTIONS TO THEORETICAL PHYSICS AS A TEACHER AND ORIGINATOR OF IDEAS AND FOR LEADERSHIP OF THE LOS ALAMOS LABORATORY AND THE ATOMIC ENERGY PROGRAM DURING CRITICAL YEARS.

The President greeted the gathering of more than forty scientific and government leaders. He lauded Oppenheimer on his high standards of achievement during World War II. Then he went on to say:

> Since the war, you have continued to lead in the search for knowledge, and you have continued to build on the major breakthrough achieved by Enrico Fermi on this day in 1942. You have led in developing an outstanding school of theoretical physics in the United States of America. . . .

Oppenheimer, overcome with emotion, grasped his wife's hand as the President spoke. When Johnson finished, Oppenheimer studied the citation. Then in a soft low voice he spoke of the "brotherly spirit of science" and he quoted President Roosevelt, who a few days before his death had spoken of all men living together, in the same world, at peace.

His voice grew softer. He paused and studied the citation again. After a few moments of silence, he looked up, then in a voice barely audible said, "I think it just possible, Mr. President, that it has taken some charity and some courage for you to make this award today. That seems to me a good augury for all our futures."

But for Robert Oppenheimer little future remained. On April 22, 1964, J Robert Oppenheimer celebrated his sixtieth birthday. As a special birthday tribute four physicists from the Institute for Advanced Study—Freeman Dyson, Abraham Pais, Bengt Stromgren, and Chen Ning Yang—wrote a special intro-

178   J ROBERT OPPENHEIMER

ductory tribute to the April 1964 issue of *Reviews of Modern Physics.*

> The authors of the articles in this issue join us in wishing him many more fruitful years in which he will continue to give to physics his insight, to physicists his leadership, and to humanity at large his wisdom.

Then as an added surprise, eighty-one year old Max Born sent a letter of reminiscences and congratulations, and it too was published in the April issue.

After reviewing the years when he first met and worked with Oppenheimer, Born writes:

> Since those days in 1926 I have not seen you again, and while I have remained in the narrow domain of university life you have taken a leading part in great historical events. I have followed your public career with deep interest and sympathy, not only because you proved to be a leader of men and a most efficient administrator, but because I felt that you were burdened with a responsibility almost too heavy for a human being. . . .

Robert Oppenheimer had never stated his feelings on his role in the atomic bomb development. After the article, Robert expressed his feelings in a letter to Max Born:

THE INSTITUTE FOR ADVANCED STUDY
Office of the Director
Princeton, New Jersey

16 April 1964

Dear Professor Born:

> A few days ago I was astonished and touched when my colleagues, at a small dinner, gave me the April issue of the *Reviews of Modern Physics.* With all the opera showing the diversity and vigor of theoretical physics today, I was surely most pleased and moved by your warm and generous message. This is not only because of my debt to you for the old days in Göttingen. Over the years, I have felt a certain disapproval on your part for much I have done. This has always seemed to me quite natural, for it is a sentiment that I share; for this reason the words you wrote were doubly welcome.

That same year Robert Oppenheimer was named Hitchcock Foundation Professor for 1964 at the University of California at Berkeley. The series of three public talks, on the general subject of Niels Bohr and His Times, included lectures on Atomic Theory (April 23), Complementarity (April 28), and The Atomic Bomb (April 30).

Many of Robert's old friends welcomed the opportunity to see "Oppie" again. But, said Philosopher Will Dennes, "Oppie was clearly not well. He was thin, tense, chain-smoking—worn. But he was as alert as ever, kind as ever, interested as always in helping the young men doing work in math and physics. He had always been willing to help young men and women to further their creativity."

In May, Robert and Kitty Oppenheimer visited Los Alamos. It was an official trip for Robert and during his stay he delivered one lecture. Much had changed in nineteen years. The Los Alamos he knew no longer existed. Most of the old Tech Area buildings had been demolished and the Laboratory had been shifted across Los Alamos Canyon. A bridge now separated the Laboratory from the "town," which by 1964 had become a good-sized "city." Few of the old buildings remained, and one had been set up as a museum. "He had tears in his eyes as he stared out across the Jemez Mountains," recalls an observer.

Robert Oppenheimer returned to the Institute. One project occupied his attention, the new library. According to several men at the Institute, "It took some doing to get the library done, and the 'doing' was mostly Robert's." Abraham Pais said of the new 40,000 volume library, "This is Robert's building."

In the winter of 1966 Oppenheimer had a severe cold and sore throat—sinus infection. When it refused to leave him, the doctor had Robert admitted to New York Hospital (Cornell University Medical Center) around March 8. On the tenth of March Dr. Frank Glensi, the Chief Surgeon, operated. His diagnosis: cancer of the larynx.

After surgery Oppenheimer underwent x-ray therapy. In spite of the nature and severity of his illness, he spoke fondly and proudly of the betatron, the apparatus used in his therapy—medical use of atomic energy. "We had a betatron at Los Alamos," he told a colleague. "We used it to photograph implosions."

Although he remained hoarse from the surgery and treatments, doctors hoped they had arrested the disease. Robert returned to Princeton and announced his retirement as Director of the Institute for Advanced Study, and when summer came Robert, Kitty, and Toni left for St. John's Island in the Caribbean.

In the fall he remained at the Institute as senior professor of physics, the post once held by Albert Einstein. But it was clear to all that Oppenheimer was seriously ill. Said a friend, "He fought the illness with stoic grace. He was in considerable pain, but he went to his office each day."

Freeman Dyson tells of Oppenheimer's last visit to the Institute. "He came to participate in a discussion on the selection of the young physicists who would be coming to the Institute. He knew he would not be there to greet them."

February 18, 1967, marked the passing of the man who had never failed to say, "Science is not everything. But science is very beautiful."

In a memorial address for Dr. J Robert Oppenheimer, Abraham Pais said, "In the years to come the physicist will speak of him. So will the historian and the psychologist, the playwright and the poet. But it would take the singular combination of talents of this extraordinary man himself to characterize his life in brief."

Oppenheimer died an ambivalent man. A colleague could say, "I worked with him, but I never knew him." And yet another could say, "He was my friend, and I knew a great deal about him, and yet, I wonder if I truly knew him."

But both friends and enemies alike agree that Oppenheimer's life was full of contrasts: conflict and harmony, hopes and disappointments, arrogance and humility, affection and resentment. The contrasts are endless.

Perhaps Oppenheimer himself best characterized his life when he wrote:

> The wealth and variety of physics itself, the greater wealth of the natural sciences taken as a whole, the more familiar, yet still strange and far wider wealth of the life of the human spirit, enriched by complementary, not at once compatible ways, irreducible one to the other, have a greater harmony. They are the elements of man's sorrow and his splendor, his frailty and his power and his passing and his undying deeds.

SYNOPTIC CALENDAR

1904	Born April 22 in New York City.
1925	Received BA from Harvard, *summa cum laude*.
1926	Studied under Lord Ernest Rutherford at the Cavendish Laboratory, Cambridge University, England.
1927	Received Ph.D. under Max Born at the University of Göttingen. Twenty-three years old.
1928	National Research Fellow at Harvard University and at the California Institute of Technology.
1929	International Education Board Fellow, University of Leiden and the Federal Institute of Technology in Zurich. Also worked with Wolfgang Pauli at the University of Zurich.
1929	Returned to the United States and began concurrent appointments as an assistant professor of physics at the University of California at Berkeley, and at the California Institute of Technology at Pasadena.
1931	Named associate professor at the University of California.
1934	Associate professor at the California Institute of Technology.
1936	Promoted to full professor at the University of California at Berkeley.
1937	Made full professor at California Institute of Technology.
1940	Married Katherine Puening Harrison at the age of 36.
1941	Son Peter born.
1941	Elected to the United States National Academy of Science.
1942	Organization began of the Los Alamos Scientific Laboratory.
1943	Appointed Director of the Los Alamos Scientific Laboratory.
1945	Daughter Katherine (Toni) born.
1945	Resigned as Director of the Los Alamos Scientific Laboratory. Returned to teaching.

1946   January 12, received United States Medal for Merit.

1946   Helped prepare the Atomic Energy Act of 1946.

1946–52   Chairman of the General Advisory Committee of the United States Atomic Energy Commission.

1946–66   Director of the Institute for Advanced Study, Princeton, New Jersey.

1948   President of the American Physical Society.

1953   In December, security clearance revoked.

1954   Hearing before the Personnel Security Board of the Atomic Energy Commission, April 12 through May 6.

1954   The Atomic Energy Commission reaches final decision. Denies clearance on June 29.

1958   Awarded the *Legion d'honneur* by France.

1963   On December 2, received the Enrico Fermi Award from President Lyndon B. Johnson.

1966   Health fails. Retires as Director of the Institute for Advanced Study.

1967   Died February 18, two months before sixty-third birthday.

PRINCIPAL SOURCES

BOOKS—General Reference and Personal Narrative

Bhagavad Gita, The. Translated by Franklin Edgerton. New York: Harper and Row, 1964.

Brown, John Mason. *Through These Men.* New York: Harper & Bros., 1956.

Carr, Robert K. *The House Committee on Un-American Activities, 1945–1950.* Ithaca, New York: Cornell University Press, 1952.

Chevalier, Haakon. *Oppenheimer: The Story of a Friendship.* New York: George Braziller, 1965.

Curtis, Charles P. *The Oppenheimer Case: The Trial of a Security System.* New York: Simon and Schuster, 1955.

Dietz, David. *Atomic Science, Bombs and Power.* New York: Collier Books Edition, 1962.

Fermi, Laura. *Atoms in the Family.* Chicago: University of Chicago Press, 1954.

Great American Scientists. The Editors of *Fortune.* Englewood Cliffs, New Jersey: Prentice-Hall, Inc., 1961.

Groves, Leslie R. *Now It Can Be Told.* New York: Harper & Bros., 1962.

Jungk, Robert. *Brighter Than A Thousand Suns,* Translated by James Cleugh. New York: Harcourt, Brace and World, Inc., 1958.

Laurence, William L. *Dawn Over Zero.* New York: Alfred A. Knopf, Inc., 1946.

———. *Men and Atoms.* New York: Atheneum, 1965.

Moore, Ruth. *Niels Bohr: The Man, His Science and The World They Changed.* New York: Alfred A. Knopf, Inc., 1966.

Oppenheimer, J Robert. "The Atomic Age." *The Scientists Speak,* ed. Warren Weaver. New York: Boni & Gaer, 1947.

———. "The Growth of Science and the Structure of Culture." *Science and the Modern Mind,* ed. Gerald Holton. Boston, Massachusetts: Beacon Press, 1958.

———. *Knowledge and the Structure of Culture.* Poughkeepsie, New York: Vassar College, 1958.

———. "The New Weapons: The Turn of the Screw." *One World or None,* ed. Dexter Masters and Katherine Way. New York: Whittlesey House, McGraw-Hill Book Co., Inc., 1946.

———. *The Open Mind.* New York: Simon and Schuster, 1955.

———. "The Relation of Research to the Liberal University." *Freedom and the University.* Ithaca, New York: Cornell University Press, 1950.

————. "Science Values and the Human Community." *Issues in University Education,* ed. Charles Frankel. New York: Harper & Bros., 1959.

Oppenheimer, J Robert. *Science and the Common Understanding.* London: Oxford University Press, 1954.

————. "Scientific Foundations for World Order." *Foundations for World Order.* Social Science Foundation, University of Denver. Denver, Colorado: University of Denver Press, 1949.

————. *Some Reflections on Science and Culture.* Chapel Hill: University of North Carolina, 1960.

————. "Talk to Undergraduates." *Frontiers in Science,* ed. Edward Hutchings, Jr. New York: Basic Books, 1958.

————. "Theory Versus Practice in American Values and Performance." *The American Style,* ed. Elting E. Morrison. New York: Harper & Bros., 1958.

————. *The Flying Trapeze: The Three Crises for Physicists.* London: Oxford University Press, 1964.

————. "On Science and Culture." *Understanding Education,* ed. L. A. Fiedler and J. Vinocur. New York: St. Martin's Press, Inc., 1963.

————. "Physics." *Listen to Leaders in Science,* ed. A. Love and J. S. Childers. New York: David McKay, 1965.

————. "The Tree of Knowledge." *Points of Departure,* ed. Arthur J. Carr and William Steinhoff. New York: Harper & Bros., 1960.

————. "We Know Too Much for One Man to Know Much." *A Treasury of Great American Speeches,* ed. Charles Hurd. New York: Hawthorn Books, Inc., 1959.

Pringle, Patrick. *Great Discoveries in Modern Science.* New York: Roy Publishers, 1955.

Rouze, Michel. *Robert Oppenheimer: The Man and His Theories.* Translated by Patrick Evans. New York: Paul S. Eriksson, Inc., 1965.

Teller, Edward, with Allen Brown. *The Legacy of Hiroshima.* New York: Doubleday & Co., 1962.

Wharton, Michael. *A Nation's Security: The Case of Dr. J Robert Oppenheimer.* London: Secker & Warburg, 1955.

HISTORY

Almond, Gabriel A. *The Appeals of Communism.* Princeton, New Jersey: Princeton University Press, 1954.

Butow, Robert J. *Japan's Decision to Surrender.* Hoover Library Publication No. 24, Palo Alto, California: Stanford University Press, 1954.

Churchill, Winston. *The Second World War*. New York: Houghton Mifflin Co., 1948.

Draper, Theodore. *The Roots of American Communism*. New York: Viking Press, 1957.

Gowing, Margaret. *Britain and Atomic Energy 1939–1945*. New York: St. Martin's Press, Inc., 1964.

Hewlett, Richard G. and Oscar E. Anderson, Jr. *The New World, 1939–1946*. University Park, Pennsylvania: Pennsylvania State University Press, 1962.

Morison, Samuel Eliot. *The Oxford History of the American People*. New York: Oxford University Press, 1965.

Palmer, Edward E., ed. *The Communist Problem in America, A Book of Readings*. New York: Thomas Y. Crowell, 1951.

Schlesinger, Arthur M., Jr. *The Politics of Hope*. Cambridge, Massachusetts: The Riverside Press, 1962.

————. "The U. S. Communist Party." *The Communist Problem in America, A Book of Readings*, ed. Edward E. Palmer. New York: Crowell, 1951.

————. "The Communist Challenge to America." *The Communist Problem in America, A Book of Readings*, ed., Edward E. Palmer. New York: Crowell, 1951.

Shirer, William L. *The Rise and Fall of the Third Reich*. New York: Simon and Schuster, 1960.

Truman, Harry S *Memoirs. Years of Decisions; Years of Trial and Hope*. 2 vols. New York: Doubleday & Co., 1958.

Warren, Frank A., III. *Liberals and Communism*. Bloomington, Indiana: Indiana University Press, 1966.

GOVERNMENT PUBLICATIONS AND PUBLIC DOCUMENTS

Hawkins, David. *Manhattan District, Project Y, The Los Alamos Project*. Vol. I. Los Alamos, New Mexico: University of California and the United States Atomic Energy Commission, 1945. Los Alamos Scientific Laboratory Report LAMS—2532, unclassified version of the main volume.

United States Atomic Energy Commission. *Historical Document Number 276*. Washington, D.C. (unpublished).

————. *Historical Document Number 214*. Washington, D.C. (unpublished).

————. *In the Matter of J Robert Oppenheimer. Texts of Principal Documents and Letters of Personnel Security Board*. Washington, D.C.: Government Printing Office, 1954.

————. *In the Matter of J Robert Oppenheimer. Transcript of*

Hearing Before Personnel Security Board. Washington, D.C.:
  Government Printing Office, 1954.
United States Department of State: *The International Control of
  Atomic Energy; Growth of a Policy.* Washington, D.C., 1946.
————. *The International Control of Atomic Energy; Policy at the
  Crossroads.* Washington, D.C., 1948.
————. *Documents on Disarmament, 1945–1959.* Vols. I and II.
  Washington, D.C., 1960.
————. *Foreign Relations of the United States: Diplomatic Papers,
  The Potsdam Conference, 1945.* Washington, D.C., 1961.

JOURNALS AND MAGAZINES

Almost one hundred articles about or by J Robert Oppenheimer have
appeared in print. Because of the magnitude of this list, only the
sources used in this book are listed.

Alsop, Joseph & Stewart. "We Accuse." *Harper's Magazine,* CCIX,
  No. 1253 (October 1954), 25–45.
Bethe, Hans A. "Oppenheimer: Where He Was There Was Always
  Life and Excitement." *Science,* 155, No. 3766 (March 3, 1967).
Brode, Bernice. "Tales of Los Alamos." *Los Alamos Scientific Lab-
  oratory Community News,* (June 2, 1960, through September
  22, 1960).
Coughlan, Robert. "Oppenheimer and Teller." *Life,* Vol. 55, No. 24
  (December 13, 1963).
Darrow, Karl K. "The Quantum Theory." *Scientific American,*
  (March 1952).
"Editorial: The Oppenheimer Case." *Bulletin of the Atomic Scien-
  tists,* X, No. 5 (May 1954).
Einstein, A.; A. Margeneau; W. Meissner; A. Sommerfield; and
  F. Bopp. "Fifty Years of Quantum Theory." *Science,* 113, No.
  2926 (January 26, 1951).
"The Eternal Apprentice." *Time,* LII, No. 19 (November 8, 1948),
  70–81.
"The First Twenty Years at Los Alamos, January, 1943–January,
  1963." Anniversary History. *LASL News.*
Hahn, Otto. "The Discovery of Fission." *Scientific American,*
  CXCVIII (February 1958).
Kalven, Harry, Jr. "The Case of J Robert Oppenheimer Before the
  Atomic Energy Commission." *Bulletin of the Atomic Scientists,*
  X, No. 7 (September 1954).
Kennan, George Frost. "The Illusion of Security." *Atlantic Monthy,*
  (August 1954).

Oppenheimer, J Robert. "Crossing," *Hound and Horn*, 1, No. 4. Cambridge, Mass. (June 1928).

———. "The Added Cubit." Excerpts from address given at the National Book Awards, 1963. *Author and Journalist*, Vol. 48, No. 4 (April 1963). The Farrar Publishing Co., Washington, D.C.

———. "On Science and Culture." *Encounter*, XIX, No. 4 (October 1962).

"J Robert Oppenheimer." *The Atom*, 4, No. 3. Los Alamos Scientific Laboratory (March 1967).

"To J Robert Oppenheimer on His Sixtieth Birthday." *Reviews of Modern Physics*, Vol. 36, No. 2 (April 1964).

Pais, Abraham, Glenn T. Seaborg, Robert Serber, and Victor Weisskopf. "A Memorial to Oppenheimer." *Physics Today*, Vol. 20, No. 10 (October 1967).

Savage, John and Barbara Storms. "Reach to the Unknown—The Trinity Story—July 16, 1945." *The Atom*, Los Alamos Scientific Laboratory (July 16, 1965).

Schiff, Leonard I. "J Robert Oppenheimer—Scientist, Public Servant." *Physics Today*, (April 1967).

Schlesinger, Arthur M., Jr. "The Oppenheimer Case." *Atlantic Monthly*, No. 4 (October 1954).

Storms, Barbara. "Reach to the Unknown, The Trinity Story, July 16, 1945." Special anniversary issue of *The Atom*. Los Alamos Scientific Laboratory (July 16, 1965).

NEWSPAPERS

"Oppenheimer, the 'Father of the Atomic Bomb,' Was a Baffling, Complex Man." *The New York Times*, (February 20, 1967).

Sawyer, Ronald. "More Than Security." *Christian Science Monitor*, (July 8, 1954).

———. "Security—Negative and Positive." *Christian Science Monitor*, (August 5, 1954).

The Washington Post, (July 25, 1954).

OTHER SOURCES

Bethe, Hans A., Henry DeWolf Smyth, and George F. Kennan. *Three Tributes to J Robert Oppenheimer*. Princeton, New Jersey: The Institute For Advanced Study, (1967).

Birge, Raymond T. *History of the Physics Department, University of California*, Vols. I, II, and III, (1967).

CREDITS

For permission to quote from published works, grateful acknowledgment is made to:

Harcourt, Brace and World, Inc.—for brief quotes from *Brighter Than A Thousand Suns* by Robert Jungk, copyright 1958.

Harper & Brothers—for quotations from *Through These Men* by John Mason Brown, copyright 1956; and for quotations from *Now It Can Be Told* by Leslie R. Groves, copyright 1962.

Alfred A. Knopf, Inc.—for a passage from *Dawn Over Zero, The Story of the Atom Bomb* by William L. Laurence, copyright 1946.

The Pennsylvania State University Press—for passages and quotations from *The New World* by Richard G. Hewlett and Oscar E. Anderson, Jr., copyright 1962.

Simon and Schuster—for passages from *The Open Mind* by J Robert Oppenheimer, copyright 1955; and for quotations from *The Oppenheimer Case* by Charles P. Curtis, copyright 1955.

Atlantic Monthly—for quotations from "The Oppenheimer Case" by Arthur M. Schlesinger, Jr., copyright October, 1954; and for quotations from "The Illusion of Security" by George F. Kennan, copyright August, 1954.

The Atom—for passages and quotations from "Reach to the Unknown—The Trinity Story" by Barbara Storms, copyright July 16, 1965, by the Los Alamos Scientific Laboratory, Los Alamos, New Mexico.

The ECS Reporter—for passages from "Remembering Oppenheimer," published by the Ethical Culture Schools, April 28, 1967.

Harper's Magazine—for quotations from "We Accuse" by Joseph and Stewart Alsop, copyright October, 1954.

The LASL News—for quotations and passages from "Tales of Los Alamos" by Bernice Brode, June 2 to September 22, 1960; and for quotations from "The First Twenty Years at Los Alamos," 1963.

Life Magazine—for quotations from "Oppenheimer and Teller" by Robert Coughlan, copyright December 13, 1963.

Physics Today—for passages from "J Robert Oppenheimer—Scientist, Public Servant" by Leonard I. Schiff, copyright April, 1967; and for passages and quotations from "A Memorial To Oppenheimer" by Abraham Pais, Glenn T. Seaborg, Robert Serber, and Victor Weisskopf, copyright October, 1967.

Reviews of Modern Physics—for quotations from "To J Robert Oppenheimer on His Sixtieth Birthday" copyright April, 1964.

Science—for quotations and passages from "Oppenheimer: Where He Was There Was Always Life and Excitement" by Hans A. Bethe, copyright March 3, 1967 by the American Association for the Advancement of Science.

Time Magazine—for quotations from "The Eternal Apprentice," copyright, November 8, 1948.

The *Washington Post*—for passages from an article, copyright, July 25, 1954.

INDEX